FOREWORD

This *Glossary* is a companion volume to a series of Handbooks of UK Wastewater Practice, which is being published by the Institution of Water and Environmental Management (IWEM), a corporate learned society and examining body representing the interests of engineers and scientists and other professionally qualified personnel working in the various sectors of the environment: water, air and land.

IWEM was formed in July 1987 by the unification of three eminent organizations, The Institution of Public Health Engineers, The Institution of Water Engineers and Scientists, and The Institute of Water Pollution Control, each having a history of some 100 years. Over the years the predecessor bodies have produced definitive manuals and other publications, notably in respect of British practice in the water industry. These have become reference sources for those who are actively engaged in the field, as well as for students seeking authoritative guidance in preparing for professional qualifications. Such publications are being continued by IWEM, and the range is being extended to take account of the wider environmental interests which the new organization embraces.

The terms in this *Glossary* relate specifically to UK wastewater practice, comprising institutions, special equipment and waste constituents. Reference should be made to other glossaries for terms of a general technical nature or as used in management, engineering and law. Some trade names have been included where used for well-known processes, but no attempt has been made to include a comprehensive list of trade names. Archaic or outdated terms have been omitted except where relevant processes or plant are still operative. Entries for manufacturing processes have been retained.

This edition is an extension and update of an earlier volume published in 1975 by the former Institute of Water Pollution Control. It therefore represents the work of many present and past members of the Institution as well as containing information drawn from publications consulted during the preparation of the first *Glossary*. These include the Journals of the Institution of Water and Environmental Management and of the former Institute of Water Pollution Control, Manuals of British Practice in Water Pollution Control and publications of the British Standards Institution, Water Research Centre and Technical Committees.

This *Glossary* has been revised by Keith Swanwick with the help of contributions from Alex Blair, Arthur Boon, Alan Bruce, George Eden, Geoff Greaves, Malcolm Haigh, Nick Sambidge, David Stanley and Gordon Wheale. The Institution wishes to record its most sincere thanks to them and to all members who have assisted.

H.D.M. Speed
President

July 1993

A

abattoir wastes. *See* **slaughterhouse wastes**.

ABC process. A process of chemical precipitation, patented in 1868 and used at Kingston upon Thames for many years. Fourteen substances were specified at first but these were subsequently reduced to aluminoferric, blood, charcoal and clay. Also called 'Native Guano Process'.

abiotic components. The non-living components of a system. cf. **biota**.

AB process. A two-stage activated-sludge process for the treatment of screened and degritted sewage without preliminary sedimentation.

ABS. Alkyl benzene sulphonate, an anionic surfactant. *See* **surfactant**.

absorption. The passage of a substance into the cell contents of an organism (as distinct from 'adsorption'). Also the uptake of a liquid or gas by a permeable material.

Acarina. Mites, some of which are present in biological filters; one family (Hydracarina) is found in truly aquatic habitats.

acclimation. The process of adaptation of organisms to specified environmental conditions modified for experimental purposes.

acclimatization. The process of adaptation to natural climatic changes or to changed conditions imposed by man, such as the presence of a new industrial waste in a sewage or receiving water.

accuracy. How closely the result obtained meets the target. *See* **precision**.

Achorutes subviaticus. *See Hypogastrura viatica.*

acid cracking process. Method of removing grease from wool-scouring liquor, involving the following processes: (a) sulphuric acid added to acidify to pH 3.3-3.4 the liquor in seak tanks to neutralize alkalinity, the grease either floating or settling; (b) grease removed by passing liquid portion through straining filter; (c) greasy sludge run on to a magma filter to drain; (d) sludge shovelled into canvas bags, forming puddings, and pressed in a steam-heated press to extract grease; (e) grease purified by heating with sulphuric acid. Wastewaters include liquor from seak tanks and that draining from magma filters.

acidity. The capacity of a water to neutralize alkalinity, i.e. to react with hydroxyl ions. Industrial wastewaters with a high acidity may have an injurious effect on the fabric of sewers, inhibit biological treatment processes, and are potentially dangerous to workmen.

acid pickling. *See* **pickling**.

activated carbon. Carbon from which hydrocarbons have been removed to increase its powers of adsorption. It encloses cavities or pores which are comparable in size to the molecules of an organic substance and in this structural form a large surface area can be contained in quite small volumes of matter, e.g. an internal area of more than 1000 square metres is often contained in less than one gramme of the substance. The size and structure of the pores is largely determined by the characteristics of the material used in the initial carbonization process. Employed as a deodorant and in removing residues of organic matter from potable waters and sewage effluents. The spent activated carbon may be regenerated, usually by heat.

activated carbon treatment. A process for removing residues of organic matter from raw or polluted water by adsorption on to activated carbon.

activated sludge. A flocculent microbial mass of bacteria, protozoa and other micro-organisms with a significant proportion of inert debris, produced when sewage is continuously aerated.

activated-sludge process. A method of treating sewage discovered by E. Ardern and W. T. Lockett in 1913, working under the direction of Dr. G. J. Fowler. A mixture of sewage and activated sludge is agitated and aerated. The activated sludge is subsequently separated from the treated effluent by settlement. Most of the settled activated sludge is returned or recycled for reuse, the excess being discharged as surplus activated sludge.

active chlorine. *See* **residual chlorine**.

acute toxicity test. A test made to determine the acute toxicity of a substance or waste. *See* **toxicity**.

ADF. *See* **alternating double filtration**.

adsorption. A surface phenomenon involving the adhesion of molecules to interfaces with which they are brought into contact (as distinct from 'absorption').

advanced treatment. The further treatment of chemically or biologically treated sewage by removing nitrogen compounds and phosphate, or other soluble matter, thereby enabling it to be used directly for industrial or other purposes, or to meet special requirements such as the removal of nutrients before discharge into a receiving water.

Aelosoma. A member of the family Aelosomatidae of the oligochaete worms. Found in aquatic habitats and in activated sludges.

aerated pile. A method of composting sewage sludge involving artificial aeration of a pile of dewatered sludge normally in admixture with a bulking agent.

aerated spiral-flow grit channel. A channel through which sewage is passing, compressed air being applied at the base of the channel along one side to assist in imparting a spiral motion to the sewage. The sewage is maintained at a velocity such that organic matter is retained in suspension, whilst the grit settles and enters hoppers in the floor of the channel from whence it is removed by pumps or a bucket dredger. Originated in the USA and first used in the UK on a full-plant scale at Derby in 1957.

aeration. A process for continuously creating new air/liquid interfaces to promote the transfer of oxygen across the interface. This may be achieved by (a) spraying the liquid in the air, e.g. spray irrigation of sewage; (b) bubbling air through the liquid, e.g. diffused-air aeration in the activated-sludge process; (c) agitating the liquid, e.g. mechanical surface aeration in the activated-sludge process; (d) allowing the liquid to flow in thin films over a weir.

aeration coefficient. *See* **oxygen transfer coefficient**.

aeration period of sewage. The theoretical period, expressed in hours, during which the sewage is undergoing aeration in an activated-sludge plant, calculated by dividing the volume of the aeration tank by the rate of flow of sewage.

aeration process. *See* **activated-sludge process**.

aeration tank. A tank in which a mixture of sewage or other wastewater and activated sludge is aerated.

aerator. A mechanical device used for the aeration of sewage or wastewater in an activated-sludge plant, or of a body of water in a reservoir or river for example.

aerobic. A condition in which elementary oxygen is available and utilized in the free form. cf. **anaerobic, anoxic**.

aerobic bacteria. Bacteria that grow in the presence of dissolved oxygen. Obligate aerobes require free oxygen.

aerobic biological treatment. *See* **secondary treatment**.

aerobic digestion. A biological process by which primary and/or activated or humus sludge is subjected to prolonged aeration so that its organic content is partially oxidized and the amount reduced by a combination of endogenous respiration, cryptic growth, predator activity, and slow oxidation of residual organic matter. *See* **thermophilic aerobic digestion**.

aerobiosis. Any life process which must have free or dissolved oxygen, usually with the production of carbon dioxide.

afterburner. A gas-fired device fitted in the flue-gas system of some incinerators to burn volatile compounds without producing any smoke or smell.

agglomeration. The coalescence of flocs or particles of suspended matter to form larger flocs or particles which settle or float more readily. *See* **flocculation**.

Agreement. In connection with the reception of an industrial wastewater into a public sewer, an agreement between the occupier of the trade premises and the water company specifying the terms under which the waste will be accepted into the sewer for conveyance, treatment and disposal. See **Consent, Direction, Exempted Discharge**.

air chamber. A closed chamber connected to the delivery main and close to a reciprocating pump, providing a cushion of air which absorbs shocks and promotes a more uniform rate of flow in the main.

air compressor. A machine which compresses air at atmospheric pressure for delivery at a higher pressure. It may be of the reciprocating, centrifugal, rotary (vane) or liquid type.

air diffuser. *See* **porous air diffuser, sparger**.

air drying. The drying of sewage sludge by evaporation and drainage of water under ambient temperature conditions.

air filter. A device for cleaning the air to be used in a diffused-air activated-sludge plant. It may be (a) a filter of oil-coated fine wire mesh; (b) a pre-coated bag filter, or (c) an electrostatic precipitator.

air injection. The injection of air into long sewers or rising mains to prevent septicity. Oxygen is also used in some locations.

air-lift pump. A device for lifting liquid by injecting air at the base of a riser pipe. The entrained air reduces the density of the liquid, so that the pressure of liquid at the lower end of the riser pipe raises the water at the top of the pipe.

air receiver. A vessel in which compressed air is stored.

air release valve. *See* **pressure relief valve**.

air relief pipe. A vent pipe running from the highest point of a pump casing to discharge into a wet well, fitted with a non-return valve so that air can be released from the casing when priming the pump.

air saturation value. The concentration of dissolved oxygen in water in equilibrium with air. It varies with temperature, pressure, and salinity.

air stripping. *See* **ammonia stripping**.

air vessel. *See* **air chamber**.

air-water pressure vessel. A vessel in the cooling-water circuit of a dual-fuel engine installation, with an air cushion the pressure in which is maintained within a specified range by an automatically-operated electrically-driven air compressor.

albuminoid nitrogen. That fraction of the organic nitrogen in sewage which is readily decomposed to ammonia when a sample of the sewage is distilled with alkaline potassium permanganate under standardized conditions and following the initial removal of ammonia by distillation.

algae. Primitive plants, one or many-celled, usually aquatic and capable of synthesizing their cell material by photosynthesis.

algal bloom. The periodic development of large numbers of algae in a body of water.

algicide. A chemical used for killing or controlling algal growths (algistat).

alkalinity. The capacity of a water to neutralize acids. It is usually due to the bicarbonate, carbonate and hydroxide constituents of the water, bicarbonate alkalinity being incompatible with the presence of hydroxide alkalinity. Methyl orange or methyl purple alkalinity is usually taken as a measure of total alkalinity. Phenolphthalein alkalinity normally results from the presence of hydroxide or carbonate. Usually expressed in milligrammes per litre of equivalent calcium carbonate.

allylthiourea (ATU). A chemical added to the dilution water in the BOD test if it is desired to inhibit nitrification in a sample containing nitrifying organisms, so as to obtain a figure for the carbonaceous BOD.

alpha factor. In an activated-sludge plant, the ratio of the oxygen transfer coefficient in mixed liquor to the oxygen transfer coefficient in clean water. Symbol α.

alternating double filtration (ADF). A modification of conventional biological filtration, introduced in 1933 and first used extensively at Birmingham, in which there are two filters in series, a primary filter and a secondary filter, the primary filter being dosed with settled sewage and the secondary filter with settled effluent from the primary filter. At intervals varying from a day to a week the sequence is reversed, the primary filter becoming the secondary and the secondary filter the primary. *See* **single-stage filtration**, **single-stage filtration with effluent recirculation, two-stage filtration**.

alternating two-stage filtration. *See* **alternating double filtration**.

alternative-fuel engine. An engine which runs on either diesel fuel alone or on sludge gas alone, using spark ignition, as distinct from a dual-fuel engine, which runs on gas with the addition of some diesel fuel. *See* **dual-fuel engine**.

alum. Hydrated aluminium sulphate, $Al_2(SO_4)_3 \cdot 18H_2O$; used as a coagulant.

aluminium hydroxide. An insoluble precipitate used as a flocculating agent and formed by hydrolysis of aluminium sulphate *in situ*.

aluminium salts. Such as aluminium chloride ($AlCl_3$), aluminium chlorohydrate

$(A1_2(OH)_4C1_2)$, and aluminium sulphate $(A1_2(SO_4)_3 . 18H_2O)$, which are used as conditioners in connection with the dewatering of sludge.

aluminoferric. A chemical precipitant used at one time in the treatment of waste-waters and containing 92 per cent of hydrated aluminium sulphate together with a small amount of ferric sulphate.

Alundum diffuser. A diffuser comprising a fused crystalline aluminium/silicon ceramic, manufactured by a process which ensures uniform permeability. Used in diffused-air activated-sludge plants.

Alwatech process. A process developed in Scandinavia for recovering proteins from wastewaters, such as those from slaughterhouses and fish processing plants, by coagulation with lignosulphonic acid followed by dissolved-air flotation.

Ames test. *See* **mutagenicity testing**.

amine treatment. The addition of a long-chain aliphatic amine, e.g. stearine amine, 65 per cent $CH_3(CH_2)_{17}$. NH_2, 35 per cent $CH_3(CH_2)_{15}$. NH_2, to digesting sludge when digestion is being retarded or has been inhibited by anionic surfactants present in the raw sludge.

ammonia. The compound NH_3; in water pollution control the term is conventionally understood to mean the equilibrium mixture of NH_3, NH_4OH and NH_4^+ present in aqueous solution, the proportion of NH_3 plus NH_4OH increasing as the pH value increases. Generally undesirable because of (a) its high chlorine demand in water treatment, (b) the toxicity of NH_3 to fish, and (c) its oxygen demand in receiving waters. Synonymous with the obsolescent term 'free and saline ammonia'.

ammonia stripping. The removal of ammonia from sewage. After the sewage is made alkaline with lime, it is allowed to flow down a desorption tower while air is being blown or drawn up it.

ammoniacal liquor. A mixture of liquors produced during the manufacture of coal gas, mainly tar and liquor condensing in the hydraulic and foul mains, together with liquor from the condensers and scrubber. Liquor may be distilled for production of ammonia, which is absorbed in sulphuric acid, leaving 'spent liquor'; the gas is then cooled and the liquor which condenses is called 'gas liquor'.

ammoniacal liquor plant. A plant in which crude ammoniacal liquor from the distillation of coal is distilled in a current of steam, when the ammonia, hydrogen sulphide and hydrogen cyanide are driven off, leaving 'spent liquor'.

ammoniacal nitrogen. Nitrogen present as ammonia and ammonium ion. *See* **ammonia**.

Amoeba. A protozoan of the class Rhizopoda, which moves by the formation of temporary protrusions (pseudopodia).

ampholyte. An electrolyte which has both acidic and basic properties.

anabolism. *See* **metabolism**.

anaerobic. A condition in which oxygen is not available in the form of dissolved oxygen or nitrate/nitrite. cf. *aerobic*, *anoxic*.

anaerobic bacteria. Bacteria which grow in the absence of dissolved oxygen. cf. facultative anaerobic bacteria. Oxygen available from sulphate is used by facultative anaerobic bacteria to respire with the formation of hydrogen sulphide.

anaerobic decomposition. The degradation of organic matter under anaerobic conditions by non-methanogenic bacteria (putrefaction) to (mainly) lower fatty acids, and the possible further degradation of these products by methanogenic bacteria to methane, carbon dioxide and other substances, the residue consisting of the more stable portion of the degradable organic matter.

anaerobic digestion. Normally a controlled process of anaerobic decomposition of sludge or of a strong organic waste, first used experimentally at Birmingham in 1910. The process may be carried out at ambient temperature (cold digestion), at about 35°C (mesophilic digestion), or at about 55°C (thermophilic digestion).

analysis. The resolution of a solid, liquid or gas into its constituents.

analytical quality control (AQC). The use of blank samples, standards, repeat and spike samples to generate analytical data supporting the validity of the sample result.

ancillary. A minor constituent of a synthetic detergent formulation which imparts added properties unrelated to the washing action as such. Ancillaries are usually present in small quantities. Examples are optical bleaches, corrosion inhibitors, antistatic agents, colouring matter, perfumes, and bactericides. (To be distinguished from ancillary as used in drainage area studies)

angiosperms. Flowering plants.

Ångström unit. The unit formerly used for expressing wavelengths of light, ultra-violet radiations, and X-rays. Equal to 10^{-7} of a millimetre. The unit of wavelength is now a nanometre (1nm = 10 Ångström units).

anion. A negatively charged ion which, during electrolysis, is attracted towards the anode.

anionic detergent. *See* **synthetic detergent**.

Anisopus fenestralis. *See Sylvicola fenestralis*.

Annelida. A phylum of invertebrate animals containing segmented worms (Oligochaeta) and leeches (Hirudinea).

anodizing. The production of a coating of oxide on the surface of a metal by electrolytic action, the metal acting as the anode in an electrolytic bath. When the metal is aluminium or an aluminium alloy it is cleaned and washed before being immersed in an anodizing solution, e.g. chromic acid or sulphuric acid, in a steel tank. When chromic acid is used it is heated and an electric current is applied, with the voltage being increased in stages; the acid is reduced to chromium salts, and small quantities of aluminium and other constituents of aluminium alloys, together with iron from the tank, dissolve. After anodizing the articles are washed. Wastewaters include spent anodizing solution and washwaters.

anoxic. A condition in which oxygen is available and utilized in the form of the oxyanions of nitrate and nitrite but not sulphate. cf. **aerobic**, **anaerobic**.

anoxic zone. A zone containing a low concentration of dissolved oxygen (i.e. less than 0.2 mg/l) often used for denitrification at the inlet end of a nitrifying activated-sludge plant.

antagonism. The interaction of two toxic substances to produce an effect less than their additive effect. The interaction between two micro-organisms by which the growth of one is hindered by metabolites of the other. cf. **synergism**.

antifoaming agent. A preparation consisting mainly of a mineral oil or other suitable compound blended with a spreading agent, used mainly for controlling the formation of a foam on the surface of an aeration tank.

arable land. Agricultural land used for the growing of crops.

Arachnida. An animal class, including spiders (Araneida) and mites (Acarina).

Araneida. Spiders, a class of the phylum Arachnida.

Arcella. A shelled rhizopod protozoan.

Archimedean screw. A spiral screw rotating inside a close-fitting cylinder or a semi-circular conduit, used as a conveyor or lifting device for liquids, slurries and powders. When used for lifting a liquid, the screw is inclined with the lower end immersed in the liquid which is to be raised to a higher level. *See* **screw pump**.

Arrhenius equation. See **Q10**.

Arthropoda. A phylum of the animal kingdom characterized by, among other things, the presence of an external skeleton and several many-jointed limbs. Includes the classes: Crustacea, Insecta, and Arachnida.

Ascaris. A parasitic nematode worm of man (human roundworm), the eggs of which can be disseminated by way of sewage effluents.

Asellus aquaticus. (The water hog louse). An isopod crustacean found in the zone of recovery from organic pollution in a receiving water and therefore a useful indicator organism.

aspect ratio. The ratio of the height of a structure to its diameter, for example of an anaerobic sludge digestion tank.

Aspidisca. A hypotrichous ciliate found in activated sludge and indicative of good conditions.

atomic absorption spectrophotometry (AAS). A physical method of chemical analysis in which the sample is atomized by volatilization, for example in a suitable flame, into the path of radiation of the desired frequency and of known intensity. Elements in the atomic state absorb radiation of characteristic frequencies. The decrease in intensity of the radiation after passing through the flame is measured and can be related to the concentration of the absorbing element in the sample. AAS is often used to determine the concentrations of metals in water and wastewater because it is both rapid and relatively interference-free.

atrazine. A nitrogenous pesticide of the persistent and non-selective family of triazine herbicides. Not effectively removed by conventional water treatment processes but may be adsorbed by certain grades of activated carbon or oxidized either by ozone or free radicals according to the quality of the water in which they are dissolved. *See* **triazine**.

Atritor flash dryer. A trade name for a machine first used at Mogden for drying and pulverizing sludge after it has been partially dewatered, consisting of a high-speed rotor carrying square pegs which move between round pegs mounted on a stationary frame, the whole being enclosed in a casing into which hot gases of combustion are passed.

ATU. *See* **allylthiourea**.

autecology. The ecology of a single species. cf. **synecology**.

autolysis. The disintegration of a cell by the action of enzymes produced in the cell concerned. Also termed 'self-digestion'.

automatic closed-loop process control. A technique for controlling a continuous-flow process, involving (a) the initial setting; (b) automatic measurement of the result; (c) comparison with the desired result; (d) production of a signal related to the extent of any deviation; and (e) amplification of the signal for use in making the necessary correction by a conventional controller or by a computer. Control is automatic by the operation of mechanical or electrical units. *See* **process control techniques**.

automatic sampler. A device which takes a sample continuously or at regular intervals of cumulative flow or time over a stipulated period. Individual increments or samples may have equal volumes or be roughly proportional to the rate of flow at the time of sampling. *See* **samplers**.

automation. The control of a system whereby automatic monitoring initiates action, the result of which is further monitored to influence further action, i.e. the 'closed loop'. Normally characterized by three major factors: (a) mechanization — substitution of machines for human labour and skill; (b) feedback— machines are self-regulating to meet predetermined requirements; (c) continuous processing — the production facilities are integrated to form a unified production process.

autothermic combustion. The condition under which the calorific value of a sludge is sufficient to maintain combustion without auxiliary fuel.

autotrophic bacteria. Bacteria which derive their energy from inorganic reactions, and their carbon from carbon dioxide or bicarbonate, e.g. the commonest types are nitrifying bacteria.

auxiliary suction. A small-bore suction pipe connected to the suction pipe of a pump, through which floor drainage is drawn. Now often replaced by a small submersible unit pumping from a small sump in the wet-well floor, through a reflux valve in the wet well.

available chlorine. *See* **residual chlorine**.

available dilution. *See* **dilution factor**.

available oxygen. Oxygen that is utilized by certain micro-organisms, i.e. dissolved oxygen that is immediately available, and oxygen combined in compounds such as nitrate, nitrite or sulphate.

axial-flow pump. A pump consisting of an impeller fixed on a shaft rotating inside a casing in which the flow is mainly parallel to the shaft, the head being mostly developed by the lift of the vanes on the liquid.

B

backing cloth. A second cloth used in a pressure filter and introduced between the main cloth and the press plate to act as a stiffener to keep the drainage grooves on the plates clear and facilitate drainage of liquor from the cake. Also used on vacuum filters.

back-pressure valve. *See* **check valve**.

backwater. *See* **white water**.

bacteria. Micro-organisms, usually devoid of photosynthesizing pigment, of simple structure and very small size (average 1 μm diameter); typically unicellular rods or rounded cells (cocci), occasionally filamentous.

bacteria bed. *See* **biological filter**.

bacterial tracer. A bacterium used as an indicator of local water movements. It may be coloured, e.g. coloured colonies, and give a distinctive growth on solid culture media, and it may display an unusual insensitivity towards an antibiotic or to an inhibitor, thus facilitating enumeration in the presence of the bacteria normally present.

bacteriophage. A parasitic viral agent causing the destruction of bacteria.

Baetis rhodani. A species of may-fly (Ephemeroptera) commonly present in rivers and tolerant of reduced dissolved oxygen levels, in contrast to many other species of may-flies which are intolerant of such conditions. Consequently often present under mildly organically polluted conditions.

baffle. Used in a sedimentation tank to check eddies and promote a more uniform flow through the tank or it may be used to create eddies and turbulence such as in an aeration tank equipped with a mechanical surface aerator. A scum baffle is used for retaining scum.

balancing tank. A tank designed to equalize the rate of flow of domestic or industrial wastewater to a sewer or to a treatment works or process.

band dryer. A device for drying sludge cake, after pulverization, consisting of a heated chamber in which there are a number of endless conveyor bands of wire mesh arranged horizontally one above another. The sludge is fed on to the uppermost band at one end and is then conveyed from end to end of the chamber, falling from one band to another until it reaches the floor, from which it is removed by a screw conveyor. Fans circulate hot furnace gases in the chamber before they are withdrawn and excess moisture is removed prior to return to the furnace or discharge through a stack.

band screen. An endless moving band, usually of wire mesh, used for removing solids from wastewater. One of the first band screens was installed at Sutton about 1893. Also called a 'belt screen'.

Banks clarifier. *See* **upward-flow clarifier**.

Bardenpho process. A process for biological denitrification and phosphate removal, developed by Barnard in South Africa in 1973, and the forerunner of many present-day systems. Settled sewage mixed with returned activated sludge passes through an anoxic zone and then enters the main aeration compartment, which is followed by a second anoxic zone. Phosphate removal was later improved by adding an anaerobic zone prior to the first anoxic zone.

bar screen. A screen for removing gross solids from sewage, consisting of a series of bars, either straight or curved, often with the upstream edge of each bar being slightly wider than the downstream edge. The gaps between the bars of such screens are usually in the range 10 to 150 mm. Screens with straight bars may be set with the bars vertical or at an angle of 60° to the horizontal. Screenings may be removed manually or by mechanical raking equipment operated automatically either by a timer or by differential head across the screen. Mechanically-raked bar screens were first installed in the UK in 1888.

barminutor. A bar screen of standard design but fitted with a shredding device which sweeps vertically up and down the screen, chopping up material which has been retained by it until the material has been sufficiently reduced in size to enable it to pass through the screen with the sewage.

Barnes' formula. A formula proposed by A.A. Barnes in 1916 and used for calculating the velocity of flow in a sewer, thus:

$$V = 107 \, R^{0.7} \sqrt{S}$$

where V is the velocity of flow (m/s), R is the hydraulic mean depth (m), and S is the slope of the sewer.

beam-house wastes. Wastes produced in a tannery as a result of soaking, liming, de-liming and washing the skins. Derived from the practice of placing the skins over beams whilst lime water drained from them and the hair was scraped off. Usually highly alkaline, and frequently containing sulphides in solution. Also termed 'limeyard wastes'.

beater. In the manufacture of paper, the machine in which concentrated pulp is 'beaten' in water containing various materials, to break up the fibres.

beet sugar manufacture. The production of sugar from sugar beet involving the following processes: (a) washing the beet; (b) cutting the beet into slices, called 'cossettes'; (c) treatment with hot water to extract sugar and other soluble substances; (d) treatment of solution containing sugar with lime and carbon dioxide to remove impurities; (e) concentration of solution in multiple-effect evaporators and in vacuum pans to yield crystalline sugar and molasses. Wastewaters include water used in transportation and washing of beet, water draining or pressed from cossettes, water draining from lime sludge, condensed vapour from evaporators and vacuum pans, and wash-waters.

Beggiatoa. A filamentous autotrophic bacterium capable of oxidizing sulphur compounds to elemental sulphur, according to the equation:

$$H_2S + \tfrac{1}{2}O_2 \rightarrow S + H_2O \text{ and energy}$$

belt filter press. *See* **filterbelt press**.

belt screen. *See* **band screen**.

belt thickener. *See* **filterbelt press**.

benching. Sloping surfaces on either side of a channel, at pipe soffit level, designed to reduce deposition of solids.

benthal deposit. The accumulated material on the bed of a stream, lake, or the sea.

benthic organisms. Organisms living on the bottom of a stream, lake, or the sea. Also collectively called 'benthos'.

benthos. *See* **benthic organisms**.

beta factor. In an activated-sludge plant, the ratio of the oxygen saturation value in mixed liquor to the oxygen saturation value in clean water.

bicarbonate alkalinity. *See* **alkalinity**.

Biocarbone process. A proprietary process which combines an aerated, expanded-bed biological filtration section and a physical filtration section in a single reactor.

bio-aeration. *See* **paddle-aeration system**.

bio-assay. A test of a pollutant to determine its effect on living organisms under standardized conditions.

biochemical. Resulting from biological growth or activity, with the measurement expressed in terms of the ensuing chemical change.

biochemical oxygen demand (BOD). The amount of dissolved oxygen consumed by microbiological action when a sample is incubated in the dark, usually for 5 days at 20°C. ATU may be used to suppress consumption by nitrification.

biochemistry. The chemistry of living matter.

biocoenose. A community occupying a given biotope.

bioflocculation process. A process first used at Birmingham in 1922 in which settled sewage is aerated in the presence of activated sludge for one hour, to promote flocculation and adsorption of finely-divided solids and colloidal matter onto the sludge flocs. The effluent can then be treated on biological filters at a much higher rate than usual. The activated sludge is reaerated to stabilize the adsorbed material before reuse.

biogas. Gas produced by the anaerobic biological degradation of organic matter. The major constituents are methane and carbon dioxide.

biogenic salts. Dissolved salts essential for living organisms, e.g. nitrogen, phosphorus, calcium, potassium, sulphur, magnesium and iron.

biological aerated filter (BAF). A fixed film reactor in which a very high concentration of biomass attached to the media achieves a high level of treatment at a loading of 2 to 3.5 kg BOD/m^3.d. Settled sewage passes downward against a current of air rising through an expanded shale media of size 2 to 6 mm. Excess solids are removed during a backwash process and conventional settlement tanks are unnecessary. The process has been used for carbonaceous oxidation alone, for nitrification alone, and further developments incorporate upward flow of settled sewage, polystyrene media, and dosing with methanol to achieve a high degree of nitrogen removal.

biological film. The gelatinous-like film of micro-organisms on the surfaces of the inert materials which forms the medium in a biological filter as the filter matures, or on the mesh of a microstrainer. It may contain bacteria, protozoa, fungi and other microscopic invertebrates, and in the case of the biological filter is the site at which organic matter in the sewage is assimilated and oxidized or otherwise degraded. Also called 'microbial film'.

biological filter. A bed of material (such as slag, moulded plastics, clinker, etc.) which is relatively inert to natural processes of degradation, usually contained within circular or rectangular walls and so constructed that air is continuously present throughout the bed. In use, settled sewage is distributed uniformly over the upper surface and trickles through the bed to underdrains, thus giving rise to the development on the filling material of a biological 'film' containing aerobic bacteria, protozoa, fungi and other microscopic invertebrates, which bring about oxidation and clarification of the sewage. Essentially, the process does not rely on filtration and the bed is incorrectly described as a filter. The first full-scale biological filters were installed by J. Corbett at Salford in 1897.

biological filter loading. *See* **filter loading**.

biological filtration. A process in which settled sewage is distributed uniformly over the surface of a bed of inert material such as slag, moulded plastics or clinker. As the sewage trickles downwards it comes into contact with the biological film with which the surfaces of the medium are coated so that oxidation and clarification take place.

biomass. The total weight of activated sludge or biological film (originally per unit area/volume). Some of the biomass may be dead or debris.

biosorption process. A modification of the activated-sludge process, introduced in the USA about 1951, in which both the absorptive and adsorptive power of well-aerated activated sludge is utilized by subjecting a mixture of unsettled sewage and reaerated activated sludge to intense aeration for about 30 min, the BOD loading being about 2.5 kg/m^3 of aeration tank capacity per day.

biota. The living component of any system, e.g. of the hydrosphere, of an ecosystem.

biotic index. A numerical value used to describe the biota of a river and serving to indicate the quality of its water, e.g. Trent biotic index, introduced by F.S. Woodiwiss, which has values from 0 (most polluted) to 10 (highest quality).

biotope. 1. An area where the main environmental conditions are uniform. 2. Having a given set of ecological conditions, e.g. under stable stones in shallow fast-flowing well-aerated cold soft water. cf. **habitat**.

black liquor. When pulp is manufactured from wood, this is the spent lye from the digesters. Also applies to the lye from digestion of cotton, linen, and hemp in the paper industry.

black water. Drainage from water closets and urinals. cf. **grey water**.

blanket weed. See *Cladophora*.

bleaching. Bleaching of cotton goods to make them suitable for dyeing or printing, involving the following processes: (a) washing with water, termed 'grey washing'; (b) boiling with milk of lime in a kier, termed 'lime boil'; (c) treatment with a weak acid, termed the 'first sour' or 'grey sour'; (d) boiling under pressure in a solution of soda ash and resin soap, termed the 'lye boil'; (e) treatment with a solution of bleaching powder or chlorine; (f) treatment with weak acid, termed the 'white sour'; (g) final washing with large volumes of water. Wastewaters include spent kier liquors and washwaters. Procedure for bleaching other materials is very similar.

bleaching powder. The product of reaction of solid calcium hydroxide saturated with chlorine gas, the available chlorine being about 35 per cent.

blinding. *See* **cloth blinding**.

blood-worms. A term applied to the red aquatic larvae of the midge *Chironomus*. Indicative of organic pollution in a receiving water.

bloom. Microscopic life, often algal but may also be protozoan, occurring in a body of water in unusually large numbers.

blow-down water. Water blown down from a boiler or evaporative type of cooling system to remove solids and/or control the concentration of dissolved solids in the system. It may have a high temperature and may contain chemicals such as chromates and polyphosphates used for inhibiting corrosion or scale formation.

Bodo. A non-pigmented flagellate protozoan found in activated sludge and usually indicative of unsatisfactory conditions.

Bohna sand filter. *See* **horizontal-flow sand filter**.

bottom contraction. The reduction in the effective upstream depth of liquid due to a hump in a standing-wave flume.

bottom deposit. *See* **benthal deposit**.

bottom sampler. *See* **samplers**.

bound chlorine. *See* **residual chlorine**.

bound water. Water held on the surface of colloidal matter by adsorptive or other physical forces.

Branchiopoda. A class of Crustacea having broad-lobed limbs fringed with hairs. Includes the sub-class Cladocera (water fleas), e.g. *Daphnia*.

break-point chlorination. The addition of chlorine to water to be used for potable supply to the point where the free available residual chlorine increases in proportion to the incremental dose of chlorine being added; at this point all the ammoniacal nitrogen has been oxidized. In the presence of ammoniacal nitrogen the amount of chlorine required may be several times that otherwise needed for disinfection.

breathing apparatus. Apparatus which should be worn when entering a dangerous atmosphere. There are four main types: (a) closed-circuit; (b) open-circuit; (c) face-mask with remote compressed-air supply; and (d) face-mask with breathing hose.

brewing. Manufacture of beer from malt, hops and water involving, in general, the following processes: (a) malt dressed to remove impurities; (b) transferred to an extraction vessel, called a 'mash tun', where water at a specified temperature is added so that starch is converted to sugar by enzymic action; (c) liquid portion, or 'wort', boiled after addition of hops and sometimes sugar; (d) wort separated from hops by straining and pressing; (e) wort cooled and yeast added to promote fermentation; (f) yeast skimmed from surface and pressed, the liquid portion being returned to fermentation vessel; (g) during fermentation the enzyme 'zymase' converts sugar to alcohol with evolution of carbon dioxide; (h) beer run into casks. Wastewaters include wort, spoilt beer, cooling waters and washwaters.

British Standards Institution (BSI). A British institution founded in 1901 and incorporated by Royal Charter in 1929, its main purpose being to prepare and issue codes of practice and standard specifications (British Standards) for quality, safety, performance or dimensions for use in commerce and industry.

broad irrigation. A system, now obsolete in the UK, in which the treatment of sewage was combined with the growing of crops. Earth carriers were used with dams at intervals to direct the sewage over the surface of the gently-sloping ground. Since application of the sewage had to be interrupted whilst the land was being cultivated and crops planted and harvested, at such times the land was not available for treatment. Also termed 'surface irrigation'.

brucellosis. The disease caused by infection with organisms of the genus *Brucella*. Commonly termed 'contagious abortion'.

brush aeration system. A method of surface aeration introduced by Dr H.H. Kessener in Holland in 1925 and used in the activated-sludge process in which a mixture of sewage and activated sludge flows through a tank along one side of which there are revolving stainless steel brushes which are partially submerged in the mixed liquor and produce a fine spray as well as a wave motion in the tank, thereby inducing aeration. Also termed the 'Kessener brush aeration system'.

brush aerator. An aerator developed in Holland for use in the activated-sludge process and consisting of stainless steel combs or brushes, caulked into longitudinal grooves in a horizontal driving shaft. When partly submerged and arranged along one side of an aeration tank the rotating brushes impart a spiral flow to the mixed liquor. Superseded by the TNO cage rotor.

Bryophyta. A plant phylum containing the mosses and liverworts.

bubble gun. A modification of the air- or gas-lift pump giving aeration and pumping. Sometimes used for reservoir destratification.

Buchner funnel. A funnel, usually of porcelain, with a flat circular perforated base, used for filtering under reduced pressure.

buffer solution. A solution containing a combination of chemicals which enables it to resist any marked change in pH when a moderate amount of either a strong acid or a strong alkali is added.

builder. A constituent of a detergent preparation, usually inorganic, which improves the washing action of the active material, e.g. polyphosphates, perborates, carbonates, silicates.

bulk density. The weight per unit volume of material, expressed in terms of kilogrammes per cubic metre.

bulking. A phenomenon which occurs in activated-sludge plants whereby the activated sludge occupies an excessive volume and does not settle readily so that in extreme cases the effluent from the secondary settlement tanks contains an excessive amount of suspended matter. Usually associated with the presence of filamentous organisms.

burnt ale. In the manufacture of whisky, burnt ale is the residue from the first distillation of the fermented wort. Also termed 'pot ale' or 'spent wash'.

butter-making. Butter is made from milk as follows: (a) cream separated from milk in a centrifuge; (b) culture of bacteria added and cream allowed to 'ripen' in vats at a controlled temperature; (c) cream agitated by paddles in wooden churns until butter separates from liquid, which is then known as 'buttermilk'. Wastewaters include washings from floors and equipment.

bypass. *See* **emergency bypass**.

C

caddis-flies. An order of insects (Trichoptera) having aquatic larvae many of which live in portable cases constructed of mineral or vegetable material.

Caenis. A genus of may-fly which lives on a muddy substratum.

cage rotor. A mechanical aerator developed in Holland about 1959 by J.K. Baars and J. Muskat for use in the activated sludge process, consisting of a horizontal rotating shaft and cylindrical framework on which are mounted a number of staggered blades which are partly submerged and sweep through the mixed liquor on each revolution of the rotor. Also termed the 'TNO rotor'.

cage-rotor aeration system. A method of surface aeration used in the activated-sludge process and developed in Holland, in which a mixture of sewage and activated sludge flows through a tank along one side of which there are revolving cage rotors which are partly submerged in the mixed liquor and produce a fine spray as well as a wave motion in the tank, thereby inducing aeration.

cage screen. A cage formed of bars, rods or mesh which is lowered into the path of flowing sewage to remove gross solids, the cage being lifted for cleaning.

Callitriche. An aquatic macrophyte, commonly known as starwort.

calorific value. The number of joules of heat derived from the complete combustion of a unit of combustible material or gas, e.g. one kilogramme of sludge dry solids, one cubic centimetre of sludge gas, one litre or kilogramme of fuel oil, or one kilogramme of a solid fuel. The calorific value of sludge gas varies according to the methane content, the calorific value of water-saturated methane at $15.5°C$ and 101.3 kN/m^2 being 37.1 J/cm^3.

calorimetry. The measurement of thermal constants such as specific heat, latent heat, or calorific value. Usually involves measuring the quantity of heat, by noting the rise of temperature produced in a known quantity of water or other liquid using a calorimeter.

Campylobacter. First recognized as a source of self-limiting diarrhoeal disease in the early 1970s and later shown to be the commonest reported cause of acute diarrhoeal illness in the UK.

canning vegetables and fruit. Canning is a seasonal operation and canneries are usually situated in rural areas. Wastewaters vary widely, depending on the vegetable or fruit being canned, the preparation required and any chemicals used in processing. They include spillages and water used for transportation and washing.

capillary suction time (CST). The period, measured in seconds, taken for the interface between the wet and dry portions of a standard absorbent paper exposed to sludge under standard conditions to travel a given distance, providing a measure of the filtrability of the sludge. The test is carried out in a capillary suction apparatus developed in 1966 by the Water Pollution Research Laboratory. *See* **pressure filtration time**.

Captor process. A trade name for an activated-sludge plant containing small pieces of plastic foam to help increase the mixed liquor suspended solids concentration which can be maintained in the aeration tank.

car manufacturing wastes. Wastewaters produced by the motor industry include plating liquors and wastes from degreasing, passivation of metals, and plant rub-down.

Carbofloc process. A trade name for a process developed about 1966 in which thickened sludge, conditioned with lime, is neutralized with carbon dioxide in a gas/liquid contacting tank, with the formation of calcium carbonate which acts as a flocculating agent. Flue gas from the combustion of sludge gas or the incineration of sludge is used as the source of carbon dioxide.

carbohydrate. A group of organic compounds produced by green plants photosynthetically from carbon dioxide and water, and used for providing the energy necessary for growth and other functions.

carbon cycle. The cycle of processes by which carbon compounds circulate in nature.

carbon/nitrogen ratio (C/N ratio). The ratio of organic carbon to available combined nitrogen (i.e. NH_4^-, NO_2^-, NO_3^-, $-NH_2$, etc) in domestic or industrial wastewaters, effluents, receiving waters and muds. In the aerobic biological oxidation of sewage the ratio is usually expressed as BOD/N/P. A ratio of 100/6/1.5 is usually considered satisfactory.

carbonaceous oxidation. The biochemical oxidation of carbonaceous matter to carbon dioxide.

carbonate hardness. Hardness due to the presence of carbonates and bicarbonates of calcium and magnesium in water.

Carchesium. A colonial attached peritrichous ciliate which is found in activated sludge and in biological-filter slimes, as well as in streams and ponds, where it is a constituent of 'sewage fungus'.

carcinogenic substances. Substances capable of producing cancer, e.g. β-naphthylamine, benzidine, 4-aminobiphenyl, 4-nitrobiphenyl, 3,4-benzopyrene.

carpet factory wastes. Wastewaters from carpet factories include liquors from the scouring of raw wool and yarn, dyeing, sizing and starching, latexing, and from mothproofing and mildewproofing.

Carrousel system. A trade name for an extended-aeration system using activated sludge and treating sewage from which only gross solids and grit have been removed. Similar to the oxidation ditch but larger and deeper and having the contents aerated and circulated by Simcar surface aerators. In contrast to the Pasveer oxidation ditch, from which it was developed, it is suitable for large populations.

case-hardening. Case-hardening usually involves dipping the metal in hot molten sodium cyanide and then quenching it in cold water. Wastewaters include washwaters.

catchment area. The area draining naturally to a watercourse or to a given point. Sometimes termed a 'catchment basin'.

catchment basin. *See* **catchment area**.

cathodic protection. A method of protecting metal pipes or tanks exposed to corrosion by attaching a block of another metal, higher in the electro-chemical series, such as magnesium, to the pipe or tank and applying a low-voltage current from an external source. The metal to be protected then becomes the cathode instead of the anode, thereby modifying the corrosive action.

cation. A positively-charged ion which, during electrolysis, is attracted towards the cathode.

cationic detergent. *See* **synthetic detergent**.

cavitation. The formation of a void, or series of voids, filled with vapour, during passage of a liquid through a pump, caused by the inability of the particles of the liquid to follow the paths that they would if it were a perfect fluid. This failure is in turn caused by lack of sufficient internal pressure to overcome inertia and thus to force the individual particles to take paths sufficiently curved to maintain an homogeneous mass of liquid.

cellulose acetate manufacture. Cellulose acetate, or artificial silk, is prepared from cotton lintners as follows: (a) cotton immersed in warm solution of caustic soda and sodium carbonate, in a kier, to remove impurities; (b) cotton washed with water; (c) treated with sulphuric acid, acetic acid and acetic anhydride to convert it into cellulose acetate; (d) cellulose acetate washed with water; (e) dissolved in a solvent and spun by a dry process. Wastewaters include alkaline liquor and washings, and acidic washings.

centrate. The liquor that has been removed from sludge by centrifuging.

centrifugal pump. A pump consisting of an impeller fixed on a rotating shaft and enclosed in a casing having an axial inlet and a tangential outlet. The rotating impeller creates flow in the liquid by the pressure derived from centrifugal force. The shaft may be either horizontal or vertical and the pump may be close coupled or there may be a length of shafting, or reduction gearing, in between. A full-way pump is specially designed to enable it to deal with unscreened sewage or sludge, in fact anything that can pass through the suction pipe — it is also called an 'unchokeable pump'.

centrifuge. A mechanical device employing centrifugal force for separating solids from liquids, e.g. for concentrating or dewatering sewage sludge. Used in the laboratory for hastening the separation of suspended solids from a sample under test.

cercaria. The aquatic distributive stage of a parasitic trematode worm (fluke). A water snail is the intermediate host of the worm and the cercaria passes from the snail into the water. The cercaria then enters a mammal which in some cases, e.g. *Schistosoma*, is man.

certified reference material (CRM). A sub-sample from a large and demonstrably homogeneous sample. The analytical responses for selected determinands have been extensively characterized using a wide variety of established methods and are published in the form of a certificate of analysis. They can be used in the validation of new analytical methods .

cesspit. *See* **cesspool**.

cesspool. An underground covered watertight tank used for receiving and storing sewage from premises which are too isolated for connection to the public sewer. The tank is ventilated to allow gases to escape and is emptied at intervals by a tank-emptying vehicle. Also termed a 'cesspit'.

chain scraper. A type of scraper introduced by C.B. Townend in 1956 for use in radial-flow tanks to separate activated sludge, in which a rotating boom, pivoted at the centre and supported at its outer end by an electrically-driven carriage travelling on the outlet weir of the tank, supports in turn a side-wall scraper to which is attached one end of a scraping chain. This extends in a curve of its own formation to the centre of the tank and trails along the sloping floor conveying sludge to a central outlet.

check valve. A valve provided with a plate or disc, hinged at the top, which is opened by the flow and closed by gravity or back pressure when the flow stops, thereby preventing reversal of flow. Also termed a back-pressure valve, clack valve, non-return valve, or a reflux valve.

cheese-making. Cheese is made from milk as follows: (a) milk run into vats, maintained at a controlled temperature and a culture of bacteria, called the 'starter', and rennet added; (b) when curd has set it is cut into pieces, allowed to settle, and the whey is run of; (c) curd ground, settled, pressed and ripened, depending on the type of cheese. Wastewaters include washings from floors and equipment, including milk churns, and whey.

chelating agent. A special class of complexing agent, having two or more sites at which it can bind a metal ion, e.g. ethylene diamine ($H_2NCH_2CH_2NH_2$) can bind at both nitrogen atoms. In general, the strongest chelating agents have the most binding sites, up to a maximum of six. *See* **complex, sequestration**.

chemical coagulation. The formation of flocs from colloidal and finely-divided suspended matter by adding a chemical or chemicals.

chemical conditioner. A chemical added to sludge to make it more amenable to dewatering. Chemical conditioners used in the UK include lime, ferrous sulphate (copperas), aluminium chlorohydrate, and polyelectrolytes.

chemical oxygen demand (COD). The amount of oxygen consumed from a specified chemical oxidizing agent in the oxidation of the matter present in a sample. As normally determined, i.e. from silver-catalysed dichromate, it approximates to the oxygen theoretically required for complete oxidation of the carbonaceous matter to carbon dioxide and water. This term is now restricted to the standard test employing oxidation by a boiling solution of acid potassium dichromate.

chemical solution tank. A tank in which a solution of a chemical or chemicals is prepared for use in the treatment of domestic or industrial wastewater or sludge.

chemical tracer. A chemical, e.g. a dye (fluorescein or rhodamine B) or an inorganic salt (lithium chloride), used for measuring the rate of flow in a sewer, pipeline or receiving water, or for determining the retention period or pattern of flow in a treatment unit.

chemical treatment. The use of a chemical or chemicals in the treatment of wastewater or sludge, e.g. coagulation, neutralization, sludge conditioning.

chemical wastes. Wastewaters from the manufacture of inorganic and organic chemicals, including the manufacture of synthetic resin, agricultural chemicals, synthetic rubber, pharmaceuticals, pigments and colours.

chemically-precipitated sludge. Sludge which has been precipitated from sewage with the aid of a chemical or chemicals.

Chezy's formula. A formula proposed by Brahms and Chezy in 1775, expressing the relationship between the mean velocity of flow and the hydraulic mean depth and the hydraulic gradient or slope, thus:

$$V = C \sqrt{(RS)}$$

where V is the mean velocity of flow (m/s), C is a coefficient, R is the hydraulic mean depth (m), and S is the hydraulic gradient or slope.

Chironomidae. A family of non-biting midges, the red larvae of some species (known as blood-worms), e.g. *Chironomus riparius*, being indicative of organic pollution in rivers; other species may be found in river beds and as grazers in biological filters.

Chlamydomonas. A green flagellate, found in nutrient-rich waters.

chloramine. A compound formed by the reaction of chlorine with ammoniacal nitrogen or with amino group compounds.

chloride. Chloride is present as sodium chloride in urine to the extent of about 1 per cent. The concentration in sewage is unaltered during treatment.

chlorinated copperas ($FeCl.SO_4$). The product of oxidation of copperas (ferrous sulphate) with the equivalent amount of chlorine. Usually produced on site and used for conditioning sludge before polyelectrolytes were widely available.

chlorinated hydrocarbons. Organic compounds containing carbon and chlorine, e.g. chloroform, carbon tetrachloride, trichloroethylene and DDT.

chlorination. The application of chlorine to a domestic or industrial wastewater to prevent septicity, or to an effluent or water for the purpose of disinfection.

chlorinator. An apparatus used for dissolving controlled concentrations of chlorine gas in water.

chlorine. A greenish-yellow gas with a density about 2.5 times that of air, which may be dissolved in water by means of a chlorinator and added to a domestic or industrial wastewater to prevent septicity, or to an effluent or water for the purpose of disinfection.

chlorine demand. The difference between the amount of chlorine added to a domestic or industrial wastewater and the amount of residual chlorine remaining at the end of a specified contact period, the demand varying with the amount of organic matter and ammoniacal nitrogen present, the chlorine applied, the time of contact, and the temperature.

chlorophenol. A compound formed by the reaction of a phenol with chlorine. Many such compounds may be toxic and have a strong odour and taste.

chlorophyll. The mixture of green and yellow pigments in the cytoplasm of a plant cell which is responsible for the photosynthesis of carbohydrates from carbon dioxide and water, the plant utilizing energy derived from light for this purpose.

chromatography. A technique for the separation of a mixture which makes use of differences in distribution of the components between a stationary phase (solid or liquid) and a mobile phase (liquid or gas). *See* **gas chromatography, gas-liquid chromatography, high-pressure liquid chromatography, thin-layer chromatography**.

chrome tanning. Tanning of light leathers using compounds of chromium. After bating, the skins are immersed in a mixture of dilute acid and salt and then treated with a chromium salt. Wastewaters include spent solutions and washwaters.

chromium plating. The deposition of chromium on metal previously plated with nickel, by immersion in a plating solution. This is usually a mixture of chromic and sulphuric acids. When an electric current is passed through the solution the chromic acid is reduced. After removal from the plating solution the articles are washed with water. Wastewaters include spent plating solution and washwaters.

chromosome. One of the thread-like bodies formed in the nuclei of living cells at the time of their division and which carry the genetic code.

chronic toxicity test. Or long-term toxicity test. A test of prolonged duration (months to years) which may include more than one generation of test organisms. *See* **toxicity test**.

cider manufacture. The manufacture of cider from apples involves the following processes: (a) pulping the apples; (b) pressing the pulp to extract the juice; (c) fermenting the juice in vats; (d) storing it for up to two years during which it is clarified by adding kieselguhr and pressing. Wastewaters include spillages and washwaters.

cilia. Hair-like appendages of protozoa.

Ciliata. A class of the phylum Protozoa characterized by the possession of hair-like processes (cilia) used in locomotion and feeding. Found in activated sludge and biological-filter slime.

ciliate. A member of Ciliata, a class of protozoans having cilia. Very varied in form and habit.

circular sedimentation tank. *See* **radial-flow tank**.

clack valve. *See* **check valve**.

Cladophora. A filamentous green alga found commonly in waters. It may cause a nuisance by producing excessive growths in nutrient-enriched waters, e.g. downstream of an oxidized sewage effluent discharge or in the final recovery zone in organically polluted receiving waters. It is then known as 'blanket weed'.

clarification. The removal of turbidity and suspended matter from sewage or water, rendering it more transparent.

clarifier. A tank the primary purpose of which is to secure clarification, e.g. a secondary sedimentation tank.

Clariflocculator. A trade name for a mechanically-cleaned radial-flow sedimentation tank with a central chamber in which there is a flocculator arm and paddles, integral with the scraper mechanism, through which the sewage passes before entering the sedimentation compartment.

Clariflow process. A proprietary, upward-flow sludge-blanket treatment process using a patented, lime-based coagulant, Clarifloc, to treat crude sewage. The process has been applied to the treatment of sewage before discharge to sea as it results in a significant reduction of faecal coliforms etc.

classifier. A unit used in conjunction with a detritor for washing grit, either by centrifugal force or by the reciprocating action of a rake conveying the grit up a ramp against a counter flow of washwater. *See* **cyclone grit washer**, **reciprocating-arm grit washer**.

Clifford inlet. A tank inlet introduced by W. Clifford of Wolverhampton in 1917, originally for use in rectangular tanks but later adapted for use in upward-flow tanks. The inlet consists essentially of an eddy bucket into which the sewage discharges, the function of the bucket being to dissipate the kinetic energy of the incoming sewage and reduce eddy formation. This was the prototype for inlets used in modern radial-flow tanks.

clinoptilolite. A natural zeolite which can be used as a selective ion-exchange medium for removing ammoniacal nitrogen.

close-coupled pump. *See* **centrifugal pump**.

Clostridium. A genus of spore-forming anaerobic bacteria. *Clostridium perfringens* can form resistant spores which survive in water much longer than other faecal indicators. Its presence implies remote or intermittent faecal pollution. Some species of *Clostridium* can reduce sulphate to sulphide.

cloth blinding. Blinding of the cloth of a vacuum filter, pressure filter or Roto-Plug sludge concentrator by finely-divided suspended solids or deposited chemicals.

coagulant. A chemical added to sewage or sludge to promote flocculation and agglomeration of suspended solids to induce faster settlement or more efficient filtration. Typical coagulants are iron and aluminium salts, lime, and polyelectrolytes.

coagulation. The process by which colloidal and finely-divided suspended matter is caused to coalesce, leading to the formation of flocs and agglomeration of the flocculated matter. Coagulation may be effected by adding a suitable chemical or chemicals, or it may be a biological process.

coal carbonization wastes. *See* **coal gas manufacture**.

coal gas manufacture. When coal gas was produced in the dry distillation of coal, the following processes were involved: (a) coal heated in a retort and out of contact with air, during which gas containing volatile products was given off, leaving a residue of coke; (b) gas cooled during passage through condensers; (c) gas passed through exhauster to promote flow of gas through plant; (d) tar removed from gas by an extractor; (e) remaining ammonia removed by washing with water in a scrubber; (f) hydrogen sulphide removed by passing the gas through moist ferric oxide in a 'purifier'; (g) gas sometimes treated further for removal of naphthalene and benzol. Wastewaters might contain phenols, cyanide and thiocyanate, and included coke quenching water and ammoniacal liquor produced during passage of the gas through hydraulic and foul mains, condensers and scrubber. Ammoniacal liquor also called 'gas liquor'.

coal mining and processing wastes. Wastewaters produced in connexion with coal mining and preparation, include water pumped or flowing from underground workings, water used in washing, grading and transporting coal, and drainage from coal storage areas.

coarse-bubble aeration. Aeration through perforated or open-ended pipes, producing relatively large bubbles of air.

coarse filter. *See* **roughing filter**.

coarse screen. A screen used for removing gross solids from domestic or industrial wastewater, with spaces between the bars at least 50 mm wide.

coastal waters. As defined in the Public Health Act 1936, section 343, waters within a distance of three nautical miles (5.55 km) from any point on the coast measured from low-water mark of ordinary spring tides.

co-disposal. The disposal together in a landfill site, of both household (municipal) refuse and a limited range of commercial and industrial wastes, which may be in a solid or liquid form. Ideally the process takes advantage of beneficial interactions between the types of waste so that in a controlled site there is no detectable impact on leachate quality. *See* **landfill**.

coefficient. A factor or multiplier, determined by experiment or in actual practice and inserted in a formula, being the ratio of the actual to the theoretical. *See* **coefficient of contraction, coefficient of discharge, coefficient of friction, coefficient of roughness, coefficient of velocity**.

coefficient of contraction. With a liquid issuing from an orifice under pressure, the ratio of the smallest section of the jet to the area of the orifice.

coefficient of discharge. The ratio of the actual discharge to the theoretical discharge of liquid over a weir or through an orifice or pipe.

coefficient of friction. The ratio between the force causing a body to slide along a plane and the force normal to the plane between the body and the plane. It is constant for a given pair of surfaces.

coefficient of roughness. A factor used as a multiplier, e.g. in Chezy's formula, which depends on the roughness of the surface with which the flowing liquid is in contact. *See* **Chezy's formula, Manning's formula**.

coefficient of velocity. With a liquid issuing from an orifice under pressure, the ratio of the actual velocity of discharge to the theoretical velocity.

Coil filter. A trade name for a type of rotary vacuum filter introduced into the UK from the USA about 1960 which uses coil springs instead of a filter cloth, is self-cleaning, and can deal with all types of sludge with varying success without blinding.

cold digestion. The anaerobic digestion of sludge at ambient temperature.

coliform bacteria. A group of bacteria found in the intestine and faeces of most animals, but also present in soil and vegetation. They are Gram-negative, aerobic and facultatively anaerobic, non-spore-forming rods recognized by their ability to grow in the presence of bile salts and to ferment lactose, producing acid and gas. Also termed 'coli-aerogenes' bacteria.

Collembola. An order of small primitive wingless insects, commonly known as 'springtails', some of which occur as grazers in biological filters, e.g. *Hypogastrura viatica (Achorutes subviaticus)*.

colloidal matter. Finely-divided solids which will not settle but may be removed by coagulation.

colony count. *See* **plate counts**.

Colpidium. A ciliate protozoan found in activated sludge and biological-filter slimes, where it is indicative of inferior conditions.

combined heat and power (CHP). Refers to the use of an energy source to generate electricity with the subsequent use of at least some of the resulting low-grade heat (hot water) produced for heating purposes.

combined system. A system of sewerage in which wastewater and surface water are carried in the same drains and sewers.

combined water. Water held in chemical combination as in a crystal.

commercially dry sludge. Sludge containing not more than 10 per cent of water by weight.

comminutor. A machine, introduced about 1938, which intercepts gross solids in sewage and shreds them without their being removed from the sewage. It consists essentially of a large hollow drum with horizontal slots, rotating continuously on a vertical axis and driven by an electric motor equipped with a reduction gearbox. As the drum rotates, teeth projecting from it engage fixed hardened-steel combs; material retained by the screen is shredded by the action of the teeth and combs until small enough to pass through the slots with the sewage.

community. In biological terms, all the populations of different species occupying a common habitat.

compensation water. The water which must legally be discharged from a reservoir to meet the needs of those who used the water before the reservoir was constructed.

complete-mixing system. As applied to the activated-sludge process, a system in which the sewage, as it enters the aeration tank, is rapidly distributed throughout the mixed liquor so that no substrate concentration gradient exists within the tank. cf. **plug-flow system**.

complex. In chemistry, a substance formed by the union of two or more distinct chemical species, as distinct from a mixture or compound.

complexing agent. A chemical species which combines with a metal ion to form a complex. It may consist of either negatively-charged ions or uncharged molecules, e.g. mercuric ion, with chloride ion acting as the complexing agent, gives the complex $HgCl^+$, and the cupric ion can be complexed by four ammonia molecules to give $Cu(NH_3)_4{}^{2+}$. *See* **complex, chelating agent, sequestration**.

composite sample. A combination of individual samples taken at selected intervals, often hourly for 24 hours, to obtain from the bulked sample a figure representative of the composition over a period and thus avoid analysis of a large number of samples taken at intervals during that period. Individual samples may have equal volumes, or preferably be proportional to the flow at the time of sampling.

composting. The aerobic fermentation of waste organic matter, including organic house refuse. Sewage sludge can be added to a bulking agent and carbon source such as straw, sawdust or wood-chips up to the liquid limitation of the process.

compressibility coefficient. A measure of the variation in specific resistance to filtration of a sludge with pressure.

compression filter. A machine used for further dewatering the plugs from Roto-Plug sludge concentrators, consisting of a large-diameter drum, the periphery of which is covered with a stainless-steel mesh (forming a drainage surface), and a separate roller, the sludge passing between the two.

concentration. In chemical analysis, the weight per unit weight, or volume, of a substance.

condensate. Liquid formed by the cooling of a vapour or gas, e.g. water from steam.

condensate trap. A device for collecting the liquid obtained when a vapour is cooled below the dew-point, e.g. water from the condensation of atmospheric water vapour.

condenser liquor. Liquor which condenses when crude coal gas passes through air-cooled or water-cooled condensers.

conditioning. The physical or chemical treatment of sludge to facilitate dewatering. Methods of conditioning include the addition of inorganic or organic chemicals, mechanical thickening, elutriation, heat treatment and wet-air oxidation.

cone aerator. A specially-designed aerator introduced by J. Bolton at Bury in 1920 and used in the activated-sludge process to draw up a mixture of settled sewage and activated sludge from below and distribute it with intense disturbance over the surface, e.g. Simplex aerator, Simcar aerator.

Consent. A legal document setting out the terms under which an industrial wastewater may be discharged into a public sewer for conveyance, treatment and disposal, or the terms under which a domestic or industrial effluent may be discharged into a receiving water. *See* **Agreement**, **Direction**, **Exempted Discharge**.

conservancy system. A system in which wastewater from buildings is collected and disposed of without the use of more water to carry it away, such as one involving the use of pail or earth closets.

conservation. The preservation, control and development of water resources (both surface and underground), by storage and other means and the prevention of pollution, to ensure that the largest possible amount of water is made available for all purposes in the most suitable and economical way whilst safeguarding legitimate interests. Closely bound up with this are land drainage and the carrying out of flood control measures.

console. A part of a control panel from which an operator can monitor and control a system.

consolidation. The process by which water is removed from sludge by settlement. Also termed 'concentration'.

consolidation tank. A tank specially designed to thicken sludge by settlement. *See* **thickening tank**.

constant-head tank. A tank so equipped that liquid in it is maintained at a constant level, e.g. by a ball-cock valve fitted to the inlet or by an overflow weir.

constant-velocity grit channel. A channel through which sewage is passing, the depth of flow being controlled by a standing-wave flume at the outlet end. The channel is so designed that for any depth of flow the cross-sectional area of the submerged portion is proportional to the rate of flow so that the velocity of the sewage is maintained constant at about 0.3 m/s. At this velocity grit settles, leaving the organic matter in suspension in the sewage. Grit may be removed from the channel manually, or by pumps, a vacuum suction device or a travelling dredger. Introduced by C.B. Townend in 1933.

contact bed. A method of treatment, now obsolete, introduced by W. J. Dibdin in 1892, in which a watertight tank containing an inert material such as stones or coke was filled with settled sewage, allowed to stand full for about 2 hours and then emptied. With double contact the effluent received further treatment in a second bed.

contact-stabilization process. An aerobic treatment process comprising four stages. 1. The sewage is aerated in contact with activated sludge (the contact stage). 2. The activated sludge is separated from the effluent by settlement (the settlement stage). 3. The separated sludge is aerated for several hours (the stabilization or reaeration stage). That portion of the sludge which is to be returned for reuse mixes with the incoming sewage. 4. The surplus activated sludge receives further aeration before disposal; this is to oxidize organic matter in the sludge and thereby reduce the amount to be disposed of (the aerobic digestion stage).

contagious abortion. *See* **brucellosis**.

contamination. The presence of 'foreign' or unwanted materials in a substance. Water may be rendered unfit for its intended use because of the presence above acceptable concentrations of pollutants, micro-organisms, or chemicals.

contracted weir. *See* **rectangular weir**.

contraction coefficient. *See* **coefficient of contraction**.

controlled waters. All relevant territorial waters, coastal waters, inland fresh-waters and ground waters, as defined in the Water Resources Act 1991, section 104, to which powers to prevent and control pollution apply.

conveyor-type scraper. *See* **flight scraper**.

cooling water. Water which has previously been heated as a result of circulation through a steam condenser or in an industrial process and then cooled, e.g. by trickling down over wood slats in a cooling tower. It may still have an elevated temperature.

Copepoda. An order of the class, Crustacea, e.g. *Cyclops*.

Copa-Sac. A proprietary name for a loosely-woven mesh sack used to screen out small debris from either settled sewage before biological filtration or final effluent before discharge to a watercourse.

copperas. A chemical, ferrous sulphate ($FeSO_4.7H_2O$), used as a coagulant. *See* **chlorinated copperas**.

core area. That part of a sewer network containing the critical sewers, and other sewers where hydraulic problems are likely to be most severe and require detailed definition within a flow simulation model.

cossettes. Slices of washed sugar beet from which sugar is to be extracted.

cotton printing. Printing of cotton goods involves the application of colouring matter, thickened with starch, gum, albumen or china clay, and synthetic resinous substances, by means of stamps or rollers, followed by treatment with a mordanting solution to fix the colouring matter. With calico printing the goods may be bleached before printing. Wastewaters include spent solutions and washwaters.

cover. As applied to a primary digestion tank, the hood under which gas collects. It may be fixed or floating. If floating, the cover is bell shaped and floats so that part of the skirt is immersed in the sludge, forming a seal, and has spiral guides so that as it rises and falls it also rotates.

cowshed wastes. Wastewaters from the cowshed, milking parlour and dairy, consisting mainly of urine and wash-down water and supplemented by drainage from yards and roofs, and leakage from the dung heap.

crepuscular. Pertaining to dusk. With insects, applies to flight in the twilight or before sunrise, as with some biological-filter flies.

crest. The highest point on a sill or weir over which a liquid flows.

Crimp and Bruges formula. A formula, proposed by W. Santo Crimp and C.E. Bruges in 1894, used for calculating the velocity of flow in a sewer, thus:

$$V = 124R^{0.67}\sqrt{S}$$

where V is the velocity of flow (m/s), R is the hydraulic mean depth (m), and S is the hydraulic gradient or slope.

critical velocity. In hydraulics, the velocity at which the flow changes from laminar to turbulent.

cross connection. 1. A connection between two pipelines which permits flow in either direction. 2. A direct connection between a supply of potable water and a supply which may be polluted.

cross conveyor. As applied to tank mechanisms, a scraper blade travelling transversely in a trough at the inlet end of a horizontal-flow sedimentation tank, or in a compartment formed by the main scraper blade and the end and side walls of the tank, and scraping sludge to a sludge outlet or outlets. Alternatively, a scraper blade travelling transversely between the main scum blade and an end wall of a horizontal-flow tank, conveying scum to an outlet at the side of the tank.

cross-flow microfiltration. *See* **tubular pressure filter**.

Crump weir. A type of weir proposed by E.S. Crump in 1952 having a sharp horizontal crest with a 1 to 2 slope on the upstream side and 1 to 5 slope on the downstream side.

Crustacea. A class of the phylum Arthropoda, members of which have two pairs of antennae and several pairs of limbs. In fresh waters they range in size from water fleas (Cladocera) to the crayfish (*Astacus*). Common in aquatic habitats, including oxidation ponds.

Cryptosporidium. A protozoan parasite found in man, other mammals, birds and reptiles. *Cryptosporidium parvum* (*C. parvum*) is the species of *Cryptosporidium* believed to be capable of causing disease in man and livestock.

culture. The product of the cultivation of micro-organisms on a prepared medium.

cumec. Cubic metres per second.

cup screen. A rotating cylindrical fine-mesh screen used for removing gross solids from sewage. Sewage enters through one or both ends and passes radially outward through the screen fabric, screenings being retained on the inside. Buckets elevate debris from the unscreened sewage and this, together with the solids deposited on the screening mesh, is discharged into a hopper by gravity and by the flushing action of water jets on the outside of the mesh. *See* **drum screen**.

current meter. An instrument for measuring the velocity of moving water.

currying. The oiling of leathers in manufacture, producing oily washwaters.

cut-water. The end of a dividing wall or vertical steel plate at the point where a channel bifurcates, shaped to provide the least opportunity for the retention of gross solids.

cybernetics. The study of the operation of control and communication mechanisms in biological systems and machines.

cyclone grit washer. A conically-shaped unit used for separating organic matter from grit by centrifugal force. Water containing the grit enters the unit tangentially, thereby developing a cyclonic vortex pattern which causes the grit to separate from the organic matter. The carrier water containing the organic matter is returned to the sewage flow and the grit leaves the unit in the opposite direction through the conical reducing section and an orifice. Also termed a 'Dorrclone classifier'. *See* **classifier**.

cyclone separator. A device in which exhaust gases are made to assume a spiral motion when finely-divided solids in suspension are deposited on the walls of the cyclone by centrifugal force and then slide down through an opening in the bottom.

Cyclops. A copepod crustacean, common in zooplankton.

Cysticercosis. The bovine effect of infection by *Taenia*.

Cysticercus bovis. A parasitic beef tapeworm *Taenia saginata*.

cytoplasm. The living contents of a cell, excluding the nucleus.

D

dairy wastes. These consist mainly of water used for washing bottles, cans, churns, equipment, floors and tanker vehicles, and wastewaters from the manufacture of butter, cheese, yoghurt, condensed milk, and whey powder. They contain residues, detergents and sterilizing agents.

Daphnia. A genus of small crustacea of the sub-order Cladocera and commonly known as 'water fleas'. Common member of the zooplankton of lakes and reservoirs, and sometimes used as test animals in toxicity tests.

Darcy's formula. A formula proposed by H. Darcy in 1856, used for calculating friction losses during the flow of a fluid through a pipe, thus:

$$h_f = \frac{4 fLV^2}{2Dg}$$

where h_f is the friction head (m), f is the coefficient of friction, L is the length of the pipe (m), V is the velocity of flow (m/s), D is the diameter of the pipe (m), and g is the acceleration due to gravity (9.807 m/s^2).

decantation. The withdrawal of the upper layer after settlement of a liquid containing solids or after separation of a liquid of higher density.

decanting valve. A valve used for withdrawing supernatant liquor from a sedimentation tank or sludge-thickening tank. It may be equipped with a floating-arm draw-off, operate on the telescopic principle, or consist of an adjustable side weir.

decomposition. The breakdown of complex material into simpler substances by chemical or biological agencies.

dedicated site. An area of agricultural land which on 17th June 1986 was dedicated to the disposal of sludge but on which commercial food crops were being grown exclusively for animal consumption. (ref. The Sludge (Use in Agriculture) Regulations 1989.)

Deep Shaft process. A proprietary type of activated-sludge process in which the aeration unit(s) consists of two shafts below ground level. Mixed liquor circulates by travelling up one shaft and down the other, movement usually being initiated by one or more air bubbler systems. Aeration efficiency is increased by the increased solubility of oxygen at the higher pressures in the deep shaft.

defoamant. A material which prevents or controls foaming or destroys foam by reducing the surface tension.

degradation. Breaking down by biological action.

deionization. An ion exchange unit in which cations are exchanged for hydrogen ions and anions are exchanged for hydroxyl ions. The product is water, and the solution is demineralized.

delivery valve. A gate valve fitted to the delivery side of a centrifugal pump for controlling the pumping rate. Also termed a 'discharge valve'.

demineralization. The removal from water of those dissolved mineral constituents which cause it to be unsatisfactory for domestic or industrial uses.

Dendrocoelum lacteum. A flatworm (Turbellaria) of the phylum Platyhelminthes. Found in streams and used as an indicator organism.

denitrification. The reduction by microbial or other means of nitrate and/or nitrite to nitrogen gas.

density. The weight or mass of a substance per unit volume, expressed in kilogrammes per litre.

density current. The gravity flow of a liquid above, below, or through another liquid of slightly different density. Typical examples are (a) sewage entering a primary sedimentation tank and differing in density from that already in the tank; (b) a heated effluent discharged into a cooler water body; and (c) cold water flowing under warmer clear water in a reservoir or lake.

deoxygenation. The depletion of the dissolved oxygen in water.

dephenolated gas liquor. Gas liquor from which the monohydric phenols have been removed by washing the liquor with tar oil in a dephenolation plant, thereby reducing its demand for oxygen.

Desal process. A proprietary process for removing dissolved organic salts from biologically-treated and clarified sewage by first passing it through a macroporous resin in the bicarbonate form. A polyelectrolyte and lime are then added to precipitate calcium and magnesium carbonates, after which the effluent is passed through a weak-acid cation exchanger in the hydrogen form.

desalination. The removal of dissolved inorganic salts from water, for example, by distillation, reverse osmosis, deionization, electrodialysis or freezing.

desludging. The operation of collecting and withdrawing sludge from a primary sedimentation tank, secondary settlement tank, humus tank, or septic tank.

Desmids. Unicellular green algae, having the cell in the form of two semi-cells, e.g. *Closterium*.

Desulphovibrio desulphuricans. A bacterium which reduces sulphate to hydrogen sulphide, thus:

$$H_2SO_4 + 8H \rightarrow H_2S + 4H_2O$$

detention period. *See* **retention period**.

detergent. A synthetic chemical designed for cleaning or washing. A detergent formulation consists of surfactants, builders and other substances which improve the efficiency of the cleaning process. See **builder, surfactant**.

determinand. Test, generating data, carried out upon a sample, either in the field or laboratory, e.g. pH, chloride, BOD, zinc.

Detritor. A trade name for a grit collecting tank with a grit cleansing channel. The tank is square or circular and of shallow depth. A series of adjustable deflectors across the full width of the tank at the inlet end facilitate uniform distribution of the sewage and there is usually a weir at the outlet end. A mechanism sweeps settled grit to a sump at the periphery, from which it is conveyed to a classifier. *See* **classifier**.

detritus. 1. In sewage treatment, an inorganic grit associated with a relatively high proportion of organic matter. 2. Ecologically, an aggregation of dead and decomposing biological material.

detritus tank. A settlement tank or pit with somewhat arbitrary dimensions used on older sewage-treatment works for removing grit from sewage. Associated with the grit there was usually a high proportion of the heavier organic matter, which tended to cause smell nuisance and rendered disposal difficult.

dewatering. A process by which water is removed from sludge to form a slurry or cake. After dewatering the sludge may still contain up to 80 per cent of water. Methods include drainage by gravity and air-drying on beds, pressure filtration, centrifuging and vacuum filtration.

dialysis. The separation of a substance, or substances, in true solution from colloidal matter by selective diffusion through a semi-permeable membrane.

diaphragm pump. A pump in which a flexible diaphragm, generally of rubber, is fastened at the edge in a vertical cylinder; when the diaphragm is raised suction is created against an inlet valve and when it is depressed the liquid is forced through a discharge valve.

Diatoms. Unicellular algae of the class Bacillariaceae having a cell wall of silica. Common in plankton in lakes and elsewhere; others are benthic or encrusting.

dichromate value. The name formerly used for the boiling acid dichromate method of measuring chemical oxygen demand. *See* **chemical oxygen demand**.

dieldrin. *See* **pesticides**.

diffused-air system. A system of aeration in the activated-sludge process using air introduced into the aeration tank by means of submerged porous air diffusers. *See* **coarse-bubble aeration**.

diffuser. A porous tile, tube or similar device which produces small bubbles when air is forced through it. cf. **coarse-bubble aeration**.

diffuser rating. The volume of free air which will pass through the diffuser at 21°C and 25 per cent relative humidity under a differential pressure equivalent to 50 mm of water, when tested dry. Applied to plate diffusers, and to dome diffusers when tested under laboratory conditions.

diffuser ratio. The ratio of the total area of the diffusers in an aeration tank to the plan area of the tank. Used mainly in connection with plate diffusers.

diffusive sampling. A method of sampling atmospheres without pumping. A tube of known cross-sectional area containing an accurately measured length of absorbent material is sealed at one end and has a diffusion cap or zone at the other. When placed in a polluted atmosphere, the molecules of gas or vapour being sampled can pass through the diffusion zone and be adsorbed on the packing material.

digested sludge. Sludge which has been subjected to either aerobic or anaerobic digestion, whereby the sludge is rendered innocuous and the concentration of organic matter has been reduced.

digestion. Strictly, the process by which nutrient materials are rendered absorbable by the action of various digestive juices containing enzymes. Used in sewage practice to mean the breakdown of organic substances by microbiological activity. See **aerobic digestion**, **anaerobic digestion**.

digestion tank. A watertight tank in which digestion of sludge takes place. A primary tank may be open for unheated digestion, or covered for mesophilic or thermophilic digestion. Also the tank may be equipped for mixing and circulating the contents. A secondary tank is open and provided with means for withdrawing separated liquor at various levels.

dilution factor. The ratio a:b of the rate of flow of an effluent (b), to the rate of flow of water (a), with which it is diluted when discharged into a receiving water. Also termed 'available dilution'.

dipolar ion. An ion where opposite charges are separated by a small distance.

Diptera. True flies, being an order of insects characterized by having one pair of wings in contrast with the two pairs possessed by most other insect orders. Many have aquatic larvae, e.g. gnats and midges, and a few species breed in biological filters.

dipterous. Belonging to the order Diptera.

Direction. A legal document setting out the conditions which must be adhered to if an industrial wastewater, already being discharged into a public sewer, is to continue to be discharged for conveyance, treatment and disposal. Under the Public Health Act 1961, Part V, a Direction may apply to (a) a discharge which has been exempted from discharge conditions under section 4 of the Public Health (Drainage of Trade Premises) Act 1937, or (b) a discharge which has been the subject of a consent. See **Agreement**, **Consent**, **Exempted Discharge**.

discharge coefficient. See **coefficient of discharge**.

Discreen. A trade name for a fine-screening assembly which consists of a number of shafts, each fitted with overlapping and intermeshing discs with an aperture distance to suit the fineness of screening required. The line of shafts is set at an angle to the flow and each shaft rotates slightly faster than its upstream neighbour, thus inducing a conveying action of solid across the face of the screen to the discharge point.

disinfection. The destruction of pathogens in sewage or potable water by physical or chemical means.

disintegrator. *See* **screenings disintegrator**.

disintegrator pump. A device which pumps screenings with a certain amount of sewage and disintegrates them. Disintegration takes place in two stages, the first due to a shearing action between a fixed blade and the leading edges of the impeller vanes, and the second due to a cutting action produced between the trailing edges of the impeller vanes and edges formed on a fixed grid.

disk filter. A type of vacuum filter used for dewatering sludge on a small works or as a portable unit. There are one or more disks, each consisting of a number of segments, covered on both sides with nylon cloth. When a vacuum is applied while the lower part of the disk is immersed in the sludge a thin layer adheres to the cloth. As the disk rotates a further vacuum is applied to facilitate drying and a blast of air then releases the cake from the cloth.

disk screen. A screen in the form of a circular disk which rotates about a central axis perpendicular to the plane of the disk.

dispersion. The process of complete mixing which occurs in water flowing in a stream or pipe, or into a tank to mix with its contents.

dissolved-air flotation. A process which can be used for grease removal, for concentrating activated sludge, or as a pretreatment stage in physical-chemical methods of treatment. Flotation is induced by the attachment of bubbles of microscopic size to, for example, activated-sludge flocs thereby reducing their specific gravity and causing them to rise to the surface, from which a concentrated sludge can be skimmed. Air is dissolved in clarified effluent by pressurization and the pressurized effluent is added to the activated sludge immediately before it enters the flotation tank.

dissolved oxygen. Oxygen dissolved in a liquid, the solubility depending on temperature, partial and total pressure, and salinity, expressed in milligrammes per litre.

dissolved-oxygen electrode. An electrode used in the measurement of dissolved oxygen. The most successful oxygen electrodes are of the membrane-electrode type in which the electrodes, which may be dissimilar metals such as lead and silver (*see* **Mackereth electrode**) or, alternatively, a noble metal cathode and a reference electrode polarized by means of an external potential, are separated from the sample by a membrane permeable to oxygen and other permanent gases but not to ions in solution.

dissolved-oxygen sag curve. *See* **oxygen sag curve**.

dissolved solids. The substances remaining after the water has been evaporated from a filtered sample.

distillation. A process involving evaporation and recondensation which can be used for producing pure water or for separating highly-polluting matter from water.

distilling. Typically, refers to the manufacture of ethyl alcohol for whisky production. The process is called 'distilling' and involves the following stages: (a) steeping of dressed malt in water to reduce starch to soluble sugars and dextrans: (b) liquor sterilized by boiling, a process termed 'mashing', and then cooled; (c) transferred to fermentation vessels, called 'washbacks'; (d) yeast added and after two or three days the sugar is metabolized to alcohol and carbon dioxide; (e) fermented liquor distilled in batches in 'pot stills'; (f) after second distillation, distillate run into casks and matured before use. First distillate is known as 'low wines' and residue is called 'pot ale' or 'burnt ale'; residue from second distillation is known as 'spent lees'. Residue from mashing, after re-extraction with hot water to recover maximum amount of soluble matter, is known as 'draff' or 'distillers grains'. Wastewaters include residues from distillations, cooling water and washwaters.

distributor. A device for spreading settled sewage over the surface of a biological filter. *See* **reciprocating-arm distributor, reciprocating-waterwheel distributor, rotating arm distributor, rotating waterwheel distributor, stationary distributor**.

diversity index. Unlike biotic index, a qualitative value of species diversity, derived mathematically from quantitative data. On the premise that communities under stress undergo a reduction in their diversity, changes in water quality result in changes in the diversity index

dolly. A washing machine used in yarn, piece and blanket scouring.

dome diffuser. *See* **porous air diffuser**.

domestic sewage. *See* **sewage**.

doppler flow meter. When the liquid flowing in a pipe contains solid particles or air bubbles, the doppler phenomenon can be used to measure the velocity. Two transmitter/receivers are bonded into opposite sides of the pipe, and ultrasonic pulses are transmitted at an angle of 60° through the flowing liquid. The movement of the particles causes a shift in frequency between the transmitted and received signals which is proportional to the velocity of the particles.

Dorrclone classifier. *See* **classifier**.

Dortmund tank. An upward-flow sedimentation tank with a very deep, usually square, upper portion and a pyramidal bottom. Sewage, introduced into a stilling chamber near the surface, initially flows downwards before rising to overflow at the surface, sludge being removed from the bottom at frequent intervals. A term sometimes applied in the UK to an upward-flow tank with a much shallower upper portion.

dosage rate. 1.The rate of application of a given dose of (a) a chemical to sewage or sludge; (b) settled sewage to a biological filter; or (c) final effluent to a sand filter or grass plots. 2. The rate and quantity of addition of poison to a test solution in toxicity testing.

dose. The quantity of a substance applied to a unit quantity of liquid, expressed in terms of milligrammes per litre or grammes per cubic metre.

dosing chamber. A small tank which receives settled sewage until the desired quantity has accumulated, when it is discharged automatically, normally by a siphon system, to the distributor of a biological filter. The dose, and therefore the capacity of the chamber, must be such as to ensure efficient distribution of the sewage.

dosing siphon. In sewage treatment, a siphon which automatically discharges settled sewage which has accumulated in a dosing chamber to the distributor of a biological filter, thereby improving the efficiency of the distribution.

double side-weir overflow. An overflow with side weirs on each side of the length of sewer. *See* **side-weir overflow**.

double-action pump. *See* **reciprocating pump**.

down time. The period during which a machine is not in normal operation due to maintenance, adjustment or repair.

draff. Husk and germ of the barley remaining in the mash tun after liquor has been run off. Also called 'distillers grains'.

drag-out. In the plating of metals, 'drag-out' is the liquor from the plating bath which is adhering to the metal when withdrawn.

drain. A pipe used for the drainage of one building or of any buildings or yards appurtenant to buildings within the same curtilage.

drainage area. The area draining to a given point, which may or may not coincide with the 'catchment area'.

draw-down. The lowering of the level of the sewage flowing in a sewer towards the outlet when the sewer has a free discharge.

drenching. Process used in the tanning of fine leather in which the skins are immersed in an infusion of bran in water, fermentation taking place under anaerobic conditions.

drift. Organisms, often of either benthic or aerial origin, which are being carried downstream in the flow of a river. The number of these organisms has been found to fluctuate diurnally.

drogue. A contrivance attached by a line to a float used for determining water movements in the sea or an estuary. The drogue can be suspended at any desired depth and steadies the movement of a float.

drop-off. With vacuum filtration, that portion of the cake formed during submergence in the sludge bath which drops off when it emerges from the bath.

drought. A prolonged period of dry weather; said to exist if, for at least fifteen days, on each day the rainfall has been less than 0.25 mm.

drowned weir. *See* **submerged weir**.

drum screen. A screen used for removing gross solids from sewage. It consists of a cylindrical drum or truncated cone rotating on a horizontal axis, with the sewage passing through the screen radially and flowing away in an axial direction. Gross solids are collected on the inside or outside of the drum as it rotates and are then washed off the surface.

drum submergence. The extent to which the drum of a vacuum filter is submerged in the bath of sludge.

dry solids content. The weight of dry solids per unit weight of sludge, expressed as a percentage or as mg/kg.

dry-weather flow (DWF). When the sewage flow is mainly domestic in character, the average daily flow to the treatment works during seven consecutive days without rain (excluding a period which includes public or local holidays) following seven days during which the rainfall did not exceed 0.25 mm on any one day. With an industrial sewage the dry-weather flow should be based on the flows during five working days if production is limited to that period. Preferably, the flows during two periods in the year, one in the summer and one in the winter, should be averaged to obtain the average dry-weather flow.

dry well. A dry compartment in a pumping station, near or below pumping level, where the pumps are located.

drying bed. *See* **sludge-drying bed**.

dual-fuel engine. An engine which runs either wholly on diesel oil or on sludge gas (to which has been added a small amount of diesel oil for ignition purposes). *See* **alternative-fuel engine**.

duplex pump. A pump with two cylinders working side by side so that whilst one piston is exerting a suction effect the other is exerting pressure, the result being that the discharge is almost continuous.

dyeing. In general. the dyeing of textiles involves the following: (a) cleansing to remove greasy matter; (b) soaking or boiling in dye vats; (c) passing goods through a solution or mordant to fix the colouring matter; (d) washing with large volumes of water, sometimes containing soap or fuller's earth. Wastewaters include spent dye liquors and washwaters.

dynamic dilution apparatus. An apparatus designed to measure the intensity of an odour. It is used to dilute malodorous air with clean air until it can no longer be detected by a panel of four people.

dystrophic. Lakes having waters which contain a high concentration of 'humic' acids, such as bog lakes with a low pH which develop into peat bogs, and are also poor in nutrients.

E

easement. A right acquired legally to make use of another's property, such as a right of way over his land.

ecology. The study of the interrelation between living organisms and their environment.

ecosystem. An ecological system in which, by the interaction between the different organisms present and their physical-chemical environment, there is a cyclic interchange of materials, and light energy from the sun is trapped. Usually consists of three components, i.e. producers, consumers and decomposers. Producers are green plants and algae which, by photosynthesis, trap light energy as chemical energy which is then available as food for non-photosynthetic organisms. Autotrophic bacteria also contribute to production to a small extent. Consumers are organisms which feed directly or indirectly on producers. Decomposers are organisms which feed on dead organic material resulting from the activity and death of other organisms. Organisms active in wastewater treatment may be regarded as the decomposed component of a larger ecosystem.

eddy flow. *See* **turbulent flow**.

EDTA. The abbreviation for ethylene diamine tetra-acetic acid, used in the determination of (a) water hardness; (b) anions, and (c) many metals. This compound belongs to a group of amino-polycarboxylic acids which possess remarkable properties by virtue of their ability to form complex compounds with most cations. Used in chemical analysis and in some detergent formulations. *See* **chelating agent, complexing agent**.

efficiency. The ratio of the total output to the total input, expressed as a percentage. As related to biological filters, it may be considered in two ways (1) The percentage BOD reduction as given by:

$$\frac{L_O - L_E}{L_O} \times 100$$

where L_O is the BOD of the feed and L_E is the BOD of the settled effluent. This is usually applied to a filter designed to achieve a good quality effluent for discharge to an inland water, i.e. a conventional filter or secondary filter of a two-stage process. (2) The amount of BOD removed in unit time per unit volume of medium, expressed as:

$$\text{kg BOD/m}^3 \text{ day.}$$

This is more usually applied to high-rate filters which are designed to remove a large proportion of the BOD load as economically as possible but not necessarily to achieve a high-quality effluent, e.g. primary filters of two-stage systems.

effluent. As applied to sewage treatment, a liquid which flows out of a process or system, but more particularly the domestic or industrial wastewater, treated to a greater or lesser extent, which flows out of a section of the treatment plant, or from the treatment works as a whole. *See* **final effluent**.

effluent-quality standard. A standard applicable to (a) an industrial wastewater discharging into a sewer, or (b) the effluent from a domestic or industrial wastewater treatment plant discharged into a receiving water.

egg-shaped sewer. A sewer with a cross-section similar to that of an egg standing upright on its pointed end. With the relatively small wetted perimeter, a self-cleansing velocity is obtainable at low flows.

ejector. *See* **pneumatic ejector**.

electrodialysis. A process for removing dissolved inorganic salts from a water by applying an electrical potential across it, resulting in the migration of cations and anions to the cathode and anode respectively. By alternately placing anionic and cationic permeable membranes, a series of concentrating and diluting compartments results.

electrolysis. The decomposition of certain substances when in solution by passing an electric current through the solution between oppositely charged electrodes. The electrically charged ions of the substance migrate to one or other of the electrodes where they react chemically with the electrode or are liberated, e.g. as oxygen and hydrogen from water, or deposited.

electrolytic process. A process in which salts present in sea water are converted by electrolysis into disinfecting and flocculating substances which can be used in the treatment of sewage. Also used for other purposes, e.g. recovering silver from photographic effluents.

electromagnetic meter. A flow-measurement device which measures the voltage induced in sewage or sludge passing through a magnetic field. The voltage is proportional to the mean velocity and hence the rate of flow.

electronic density detector. An instrument employing one or more of a range of physical measurement techniques such as measurement of viscosity and attenuation or scattering of electromagnetic, sonic, or ultrasonic energy to determine the bulk density of a fluid. Such an instrument can be utilized to stop and start the withdrawal of sludge from a settlement tank by monitoring the sensing element in the sludge withdrawal pipe and thus operating the control valve at a predetermined density setting. *See* **sludge level detector**.

electrostatic precipitator. A device used for cleaning the air used in the activated-sludge process, or exhaust gases from the incineration of sewage sludge. When a high voltage is applied to electrodes placed in the system the dust particles are attracted to the electrodes and are removed.

elutriation. A process by which sludge is washed with either fresh water or plant effluent to reduce the alkalinity of the sludge, particularly by removing ammoniacal compounds and fine particles, thereby reducing the amount of coagulant required.

emergency bypass. A channel or pipe which enables a treatment unit or units, or a machine, to be bypassed so that it can be taken out of service for maintenance or repair, or if a power failure occurs.

emulsifying agent. An agent capable of modifying the surface tension of droplets in colloidal dispersion to prevent coalescence, examples being soap and surfactants.

Enchytraeidae. Pot or white worms, being a family of small oligochaete worms living in muds and other damp habitats, and common in biological filters, e.g. *Lumbricillus (Pachydrilus)*.

enclosed aerated filter. A biological filter which is completely enclosed and is equipped with a fan for providing a continuous current of air through the filter.

endogenous phase of growth. That phase of growth of a microbial culture when, owing to the depletion of nutrients or to other adverse environmental conditions, the individual organisms undergo respiration using their own cellular contents as substrate, or some individuals continue to multiply using the material of the dead cells of the colony as their respiratory substrate. In this sense endogenous is in respect of the colony rather than individual cells. In such cases this results in a decline in the population of the colony and is therefore a negative growth phase.

endogenous respiration. The metabolic respiration of a cell in which the cell contents are themselves used as the metabolic substrate, usually in the absence of an external substrate. Also termed 'autolysis'. *See* **respiration**.

engineering workshop wastes. Wastes produced by engineering workshops, often containing lubricating and fuel oils, neat cutting oils or an aqueous emulsion of solubilized cutting oil .

Entamoeba histolytica. A parasitic amoeboid protozoan which causes dysentery in man and is spread by contact with polluted waters.

enteric viruses. A mixed group of viruses with the common property of infecting the alimentary tract. Over 114 different types have so far been isolated from humans. During infection viruses are shed into the lumen of the gut and excreted in very large numbers (10^6 to 10^9 per gramme of faeces) and therefore have access to faecally contaminated waters. The minimum infective dose is low.

Enterobius. A nematode worm, parasitic in man, the eggs of which can be found in sewage.

Enteromorpha. A tubular thalloid green alga related to sea lettuce *Ulva*. Found in brackish and polluted waters, and especially abundant in polluted estuaries.

Enterovirus. A sub-group (genus) of the Picornaviridae family of viruses. Over 70 different types have been isolated from man. Their normal site of infection is the intestinal tract but other organs may become involved. Diseases caused range from the trivial to the fatal, including infectious hepatitis, poliomyelitis and meningitis.

enterococci. Coccus bacteria commonly found in the gut of mammals.

enzyme. An organic catalyst produced by living organisms which enables them to carry out complex biochemical reactions at normal temperatures and pressures. A characteristic feature of living material, i.e. protoplasms.

Ephemeroptera. May-flies, a class of insects with aquatic nymphs which are characterized by the possession of three tail-like processes. Useful as indicator organisms.

epilimnion. The uppermost layer of a thermally stratified body of water, i.e. that above the thermocline.

Epistylis. A colonial peritrichous ciliate commonly occurring in activated sludge or biological-filter film.

epithelium. External layer of cells covering a free surface or lining a tube or cavity e.g. gill epithelium in fish.

equalizing tank. *See* **balancing tank**.

Eristalis tenax. A dipterous fly with a bee-like appearance, the larva of which (known as the rat-tailed maggot) is aquatic and which can, by breathing atmospheric air through a telescopic tail, exist in most organically polluted waters and sludges when these are not too deep. Its presence is indicative of organic pollution.

Erpobdella. A genus of freshwater leeches, commonly found in streams, which are useful indicator organisms.

Escherichia coli. A bacterium living in the alimentary tract of man and other mammals. As it is passed out with faeces in large numbers its presence in water is indicative of faecal contamination and the possible presence of pathogenic organisms of enteric origin; it is not itself normally pathogenic. Also known as *E.coli*, *Esch.coli* or *Bact.coli*.

esparto pulp manufacture. Conversion of esparto grass into fibre for paper-making, involving the following processes: (a) mechanical cleaning of the esparto; (b) digestion under pressure with solution of sodium hydroxide; (c) draining off lye and washing pulp with hot water and then with cold water; (d) washing pulp in a 'potcher' with water to which bleach is added; (e) further washing in washing machine. Wastewaters include spent lye and washwaters.

euphotic zone. The upper layer of water to a depth when light penetration is sufficient to support effective photosynthesis.

eutrophic. A term applied to waters rich in plant nutrients.

eutrophication. The enrichment of natural waters, especially by compounds of nitrogen and phosphorus, resulting in increased primary productivity. *See* **eutrophic**.

excess-activated sludge. *See* **surplus-activated sludge**.

exchange coefficient. *See* **oxygen transfer coefficient**.

Exempted Discharge. Exemption relating to the continuance or recommencement of a certain discharge conferred on an occupier of trade premises under the Public Health (Drainage of Trade Premises) Act 1937. The consent of the water company is unnecessary if an industrial wastewater of the same nature or composition was lawfully discharged from the premises to the sewer at any time during the period of one year ended 3 March 1937 (the basic year), so long as the maximum daily quantity so discharged on any one day of the basic year and the highest rate of discharge is not increased, and the payment if any continues to be made in accordance with the terms of any agreement which was in force at the end of the basic year and had thereafter ceased to be in force. Under section 57 of the Public Health Act 1961 a direction may be issued by a water company specifying conditions under which an exempted discharge may continue to be received into the public sewer. *See* **Agreement**, **Consent**, **Direction**.

exfiltration. Escape of flow from a sewer into surrounding ground.

exhaust-gas water heater. A heater in the cooling-water circuit of a dual-fuel engine, which uses heat from the exhaust gases for heating water in the circuit before the gases are discharged through a silencer to atmosphere.

existing discharge. As defined in the Sewerage (Scotland) Act 1968, section 33(1), a discharge of industrial wastewater from trade premises into the sewer or sewage-treatment works of a local authority which was lawfully made within the period of two years ended on the 16 May 1973. *See* **prescriptive right**.

exit coefficient. *See* **oxygen transfer coefficient**.

exogenous. Originating outside the organism.

exopterygote. An insect in which the adult form develops gradually through nymphal stages by successive moults, e.g. may-flies, stone-flies, as distinct from endopterygotes which have a sudden metamorphosis involving a pupal stage.

expanded-bed reactor. A bed of particles which remain in stationary contact when a flow is passed through them, although they may respond to assume a loose-packed arrangement when the flow is first applied.

explosimeter. A device for indicating the concentration of combustible gas.

explosive limits. The lower explosive limit (LEL) is the lowest concentration in air of an inflammable gas such as methane at which, when the mixture is ignited, sufficient heat is generated to bring the temperature of successive layers of unburnt gas to the ignition point, at which the flame becomes self-propagating. Similarly, the upper explosive limit (UEL) is the highest concentration of an inflammable gas in air at which the flame is still self-propagating.

extended-aeration process. A modification of the activated-sludge process whereby the sewage and activated sludge are subjected to prolonged aeration; the sludge being returned at a high rate, with the aim of bringing about considerable oxidation and aerobic digestion of the organic matter in the activated sludge.

extended-filtration process. A process in which a relatively large volume of biological-filter effluent is mixed with comminuted crude sewage and the mixture is treated at a relatively high rate in a tower filter containing a plastics medium. Effluent from the filter is settled in a tank from the base of which some of the effluent containing a proportion of solids is withdrawn, to be returned for mixing with the incoming sewage. Final effluent passes through an upward-flow clarifer before discharge. During passage through the filter the solids are oxidized and stabilized — hence the term 'extended-filtration'.

F

facultative anaerobic bacteria. As applied to waste treatment, refers to species of bacteria capable of living either aerobically or anaerobically according to the conditions.

faecal streptococci. Present in faeces and therefore in sewage. Gram-positive cocci forming pairs or chains which are non-sporing, oxidase and catalase negative. They can grow both aerobically and anaerobically in the presence of bile salts and in concentrations of azide which are inhibitory to coliforms. They tend to be more resistant to chlorine than members of the coliform group.

false floor. The drainage system at the base of a biological filter, consisting of specially fabricated tiles or inverted half-round pipes resting on the concrete floor and supporting the medium but allowing air and effluent to pass through.

farm wastes. Farm wastes include silage liquor and wastes from cowsheds, piggeries and poultry houses.

feed solids. The total weight of dry solids in the sludge fed (a) to a digestion plant, or (b) to a concentration, dewatering or drying process. Alternatively, the concentration of dry solids in the feed sludge.

feedforward process control. A technique sometimes used for controlling a continuous-flow process, based on the measurement of disturbing influences which precede a deviation from the controlled condition so that corrective action may be taken before deviation occurs. A precise knowledge is essential of how disturbing influences will affect the controlled condition, and of the effects of adjustments to counteract them. The technique is usually associated with monitoring of the effect to ensure that adjustment has achieved the desired result. *See* **process control techniques.**

fellmongering. Preparation of the skins of sheep and lambs for tanning, involving the following processes: (a) washing skins with water to remove dirt, blood, etc; (b) steeping skins in lime water, or applying a special lime paste, to loosen the wool; (c) removing the wool by scraping; (d) soaking the skins in strong milk of lime or dilute sulphuric acid to prevent putrefaction. Wastewaters include liquor from soak tank, liquors from liming, and washwaters.

fermentation. A process of decomposition of organic substances (typically carbohydrates and organic acids) by micro-organisms, transfer of oxygen not being involved. In anaerobic sludge digestion, decomposition is carried out in the pH range 6.8-7.4: (a) by acid-forming or non-methanogenic bacteria which produce mainly lower fatty acids (volatile acids), and (b) by methane producers or methanogenic bacteria which convert the volatile acids to methane and carbon dioxide.

fermentation industries. Fermentation industries use the activity of micro-organisms to convert one substance to another. They include distilling and brewing, and industries manufacturing malt vinegar, yeast, cider, antibiotics, vitamins, cheese, wine and organic acids.

ferric chloride. An iron salt, $FeCl_3$, used as a conditioner in connexion with the dewatering of sludge.

fertilizer. A material applied to the soil to provide chemicals essential to plant life. The principal fertilizers are compounds of nitrogen, phosphorus and potassium, used for promoting growth, and lime for adjusting the acidity or alkalinity of the soil. Typical fertilizers are sulphate of ammonia, super-phosphate of lime and sulphate of potash. The Agriculture Act 1970 requires that the fertilizing value of nitrogenous fertilizers shall be stated in terms of their nitrogen (N) content, phosphoric acid in terms of phosphorus pentoxide (P_2O_5), potash in terms of potassium oxide (K_2O), and the neutralizing value of a fertilizer in terms of calcium oxide (CaO). *See* **manure**.

filamentous organisms. Micro-organisms with a filamentous habit of growth. Include some bacteria and most fungi, the former with much finer filaments. Algae are commonly filamentous and can be distinguished from bacteria and fungi by the presence of photosynthetic pigment. In relation to activated sludge, usually refers to *Sphaerotilus natans*, type D21N or *Microthrir parvicella*.

fill-and-draw system. A method of operating treatment tanks in the early days, involving (a) filling the tank with sewage; (b) allowing the sludge to settle; (c) decanting the supernatant liquor; and (d) removing the sludge. Used at one time in the operation of the activated-sludge process and now often used experimentally. Contact beds were operated on a fill-and-draw system.

fill-and-draw tank. A treatment tank which is operated on a fill-and-draw system. *See* **fill-and-draw system**.

filler. An organic or inorganic product, usually inert, employed to produce the desired type of presentation and/or concentration in a synthetic detergent, e.g. sodium sulphate, water and alcohol. *See* **ancillary**, **builder**.

filter aid. Inert insoluble material added to sludge to improve its filtrability. Materials used for this purpose include pulverized fuel ash, sludge ash, and waste paper.

filter blinding. *See* **cloth blinding**.

filter cake. *See* **sludge cake**.

filter leaf. A small test unit incorporating a perforated disk covered by filter cloth, used to simulate vacuum filtration.

filter loading. Gravimetrically, the kilogrammes of BOD applied per cubic metre of medium in a biological filter per day. Superficially, the cubic metres of sewage applied per square metre of the surface of a biological filter or sand filter per day. Hydraulically, the cubic metres of sewage applied per cubic metre of medium in a biological filter per day.

filter medium. With a biological filter, the material of which the filter is formed and on which a zoogloeal film containing bacteria, fungi and protozoa develops. Organisms in the film feed on and oxidize the polluting matter as the sewage percolates downward over the biologically-active surfaces. Conventional media include broken rock, gravel, slag and clinker, or a synthetic plastics medium may be used.

filter press. *See* **pressure filter**.

filter unloading. The sloughing of biological film each spring from the surfaces of the medium in a biological filter. *See* **scouring organisms**.

filterbelt press. A device for dewatering chemically-treated sludge, of German origin and consisting of two horizontal continuous belts, moving in the same direction, the lower one of cloth woven with a relatively open texture and the upper one being impervious. The sludge is fed in at one end and as it travels along between the belts it is subjected to gradually increasing pressure so that liquid drains through the lower belt and is collected in a trough.

filtrability. Amenability to solids/liquid separation by filtration. *See* **specific resistance to filtration, capillary suction time** and **pressure filtration time**.

filtrate. Liquor removed from sludge during pressure filtration, vacuum filtration, or dewatering in Roto-Plug concentrators.

final clarifier. *See* **secondary settlement tank**.

final effluent. Typically , the effluent discharge from a treatment plant after completion of treatment of a domestic or industrial wastewater.

final separating tank. *See* **secondary settlement tank**.

final settling tank. *See* **secondary settlement tank**.

fine screen. A screen with apertures of 3 to 15 mm.

fines. The finer solids in sludge which tend to remain in the liquid portion when the sludge is dewatered so that when this is returned to the works for treatment the 'fines' tend to accumulate in the system.

fixed-bridge scraper. A type of scraper used in radial-flow sedimentation or settlement tanks, consisting of a fixed bridge spanning the tank with a rotating scraper both supported and driven from the centre.

fixed cover. *See* **cover**.

fixed distributor. *See* **stationary distributor**.

fixed-jet distributor. An early method of distributing settled sewage over the surface of a biological filter, involving the use of pipes laid on or supported above the surface of the filter with jets at intervals specially designed to produce a fine spray. *See* **stationary distributor**.

fixed spray. *See* **fixed-jet distributor**.

Flagellata. Protozoa which possess one or more whip-like extensions (flagella) and reproduce asexually by longitudinal binary fission.

flame trap. A device installed in a pipeline conveying gas to prevent a flame passing along the pipeline.

flap valve. *See* **check valve**.

flash dryer. A device for vaporizing water from pulverized sludge cake through contact with a current of hot gas from a furnace. *See* **Atritor**.

flash mixer. A device for quickly dispersing chemicals uniformly throughout a liquid.

flatworm. *See* **Trematoda**, **Turbellaria**.

flax retting. Extraction of fibre from flax to enable it to be used in the manufacture of linen, thread, twine or sackcloth. The traditional process involves the following stages: (a) immersion of flax in warm water; (b) after several hours the water, called 'leach liquor', is replaced with fresh water at a higher temperature; (c) after standing for a long time, during which the conditions become anaerobic, the water (called 'retting liquor') is run off; (d) fibre removed by mechanical means. Wastewaters include leach liquor and retting liquor. An aerobic retting process may be used to minimize pollution.

flight scraper. A type of scraper used in connection with horizontal-flow tanks, consisting essentially of several blades or flights spanning the tank and attached at intervals to endless chains running on sprocket wheels supported from the side walls of the tank, two wheels near the floor and two just below the water surface. The chains are driven from a common shaft by an electric motor and the blades sweep the sludge into hoppers at the inlet end of the tank and then return along the surface, sweeping scum to the outlet end.

floating-arm draw-off. *See* **decanting valve**.

floating cover. *See* **cover**.

float-operated regulating valve. A float-operated valve which starts to operate when the sewage flowing through the chamber reaches a certain level. It then diverts a portion of the flow to storm tanks or a receiving water, the volume diverted increasing automatically as the level rises.

float switch. An electrical switch operated by a float in a sump or tank and usually controlling the motor driving a pump.

float technique. A technique for measuring the velocity in an open channel, tank or receiving water or for determining the pattern of flow in a tank.

floc. A small gelatinous mass formed by the addition of a coagulant to sewage, by flocculation and agglomeration, or in the activated-sludge process by biochemical action.

flocculating agent. A chemical which, when added to sewage, causes the formation of an insoluble flocculent precipitate which adsorbs or entrains colloidal matter and finely divided solids, enabling them to separate from the sewage by settlement.

flocculation. The coagulation and agglomeration of colloidal and finely-divided suspended matter to form flocs. Achieved in sewage treatment by (a) adding a chemical; (b) gentle stirring of the sewage by mechanical means; or (c) biological action during the sedimentation process. *See* **agglomeration**.

flocculator. A slowly-moving device which assists floc formation, usually immediately after the addition of a flocculating agent.

flood irrigation. The application of settled sewage to an area of land, surrounded by a low earth embankment, to a depth of perhaps 0.3 metre and allowing the sewage to percolate through the soil to underdrains, thus encouraging biochemical treatment.

floor tile. A specially-shaped vitrified clay tile laid on a concrete floor of a biological filter to form a 'false' floor on which the filter medium is placed. *See* **false floor**.

flotation. A process in which the specific gravity of particles of suspended matter is modified, causing them to rise to the surface so that they may be removed by skimming. Applied to the thickening of activated sludge by injecting fine bubbles of air which adhere to the sludge flocs and cause them to rise. Also applied to the separation of oil from oily wastes.

flow recorder. An instrument which records on a chart or into a computer memory the rate of flow of a liquid.

flow sheet. A diagram showing the stages in a treatment process and their interrelationships.

flow-through period. The average period required for a unit volume of sewage to pass through a tank from inlet to outlet. *See* **retention period**.

flow to full treatment (FFT). The maximum rate of flow accepted for settlement and biological treatment at a sewage works. It is expressed as:
$$Q = 3PG + I + 3E$$
where:
Q = flow to full treatment (m^3/d)
P = population
G = average domestic water consumption ($m^3/hd.d$)
I = infiltration (m^3/d)
E = industrial effluent (m^3/d)

flue gas. The exhaust gas produced during the incineration of a fuel or of sludge.

fluidized-bed combustion. A process for the incineration of sludge or the combustion of other fuels in which the material concerned is fed onto, or into, a bed of heated sand which is kept in a state of agitation and expansion by blowing air upwards through the bed. The ash is normally separated from the flue gas in a cyclone separator after combustion.

fluidized-bed reactor. A treatment process where the flow of effluent to be treated is used to fluidize suitable bed material. As usually applied in waste treatment, inert solid particles, about 2 to 6 mm diameter, are used on which a biological film can develop.

flukes. Parasitic flatworms of the phylum Platyhelminthes, class Trematoda, e.g. *Schistosoma*, the cause of schistosomiasis (bilharzia) in man. They have larval stages usually with an alternation of host, one of which is an aquatic snail.

fluorescein. A dark red crystalline substance which dissolves in an alkaline solution to produce a green fluorescent liquid. Commonly used as a tracer for measuring rates and patterns of flow.

fluorescent tracer. A fluorescent dye used for measuring the rate of flow or for tracing the pattern of flow, e.g. in a sedimentation tank.

fluorosis. The disease caused by too much fluoride in water, air or food, causing mottling of teeth and skeletal damage in man and animals.

fly ash. A powdery ash present in the hot gases leaving an incinerator which must be separated from them for separate disposal before the gases are discharged to atmosphere.

F/M ratio. The ratio of food to mass. In the activated-sludge process, the ratio of the loading in terms of kilogrammes of BOD per day to the weight in kilogrammes of either the volatile or the total suspended solids in the mixed liquor.

foam fractionation. A process proposed for the reclamation of water from final effluent, involving the removal of synthetic detergent residues by bubbling air through the water to force detergents to the surface in the form of a layer of foam which is carried out of the fractionation tank by the flow of air and is then collapsed by means of a fan.

foaming. The formation of a foam or froth on the surface of (a) the mixed liquor in an aeration tank; (b) the sludge in a primary digestion tank; or (c) a body of water, caused by surfactants and/or polyglycols lowering the surface tension of the liquid.

food chain. A sequence of reactions in which successive organisms feed on the previous one in the sequence. Usually the successive organisms are larger but fewer in numbers in the community, e.g. alga — water flea — water bug — fish.

food processing and manufacturing. Food processing and manufacturing includes canning of vegetables and fruit, pea vining, processing of potatoes, washing and packaging vegetables, preparation of frozen foods, bread making, meat processing, and the manufacture of butter, cheese and other milk products.

food webs. The interlocking patterns formed by a series of interconnected food chains.

foot valve. A non-return valve attached to the inlet of a pump suction pipe, which opens to allow liquid to enter the pipe and closes to prevent a return flow.

force main. A pipeline leading from the discharge side of a pump through which a liquid is forced to a higher level.

formula A. Formula for calculating 'carry on' flow at a storm water overflow, recommended by Technical Committee on Storm Overflows and the Disposal of Storm Sewage 1970. It is the level at which a storm overflow from a sewer is set and takes into account domestic water use, infiltration and the volume of trade effluent. It is the minimum level at which the sewage is sufficiently diluted by rainwater so as to avoid pollution of the receiving watercourse when overflowed from the sewer.

$$Q = (PG + I + E) + 1.36P + 2E$$

where:

Q = storm overflow level (m^3/d)

P = population

G = average domestic water consumption (m^3/hd.d)

I = infiltration (m³/d)

E = industrial effluent (m³/d)

foul sewer. A sewer conveying sewage, i.e. wastewater of domestic or industrial origin, excluding rainwater or surface water. *See* **partially-separate system, combined system.**

Føyn process. A process devised by E. Føyn in Norway about 1959 for removing phosphates from domestic sewage using an electrolytic cell through which is passed a mixture of sea water and sewage. Magnesium hydroxide is precipitated from salts in the sea water and this reacts with ammonia present in the sewage and with phosphate ions to precipitate magnesium ammonium orthophosphate, any excess magnesium hydroxide acting as a flocculating agent. Hydrogen released at the cathode is entrained in the flocs, which float to the surface.

Francis's formula. A formula used for calculating the flow through a rectangular weir, thus:

$$Q = 1.84\,(L - 0.1nH)\,H^{1}/_2$$

where Q is the rate of discharge(m³/s), L is the length of the weir (m), H is the head of liquid over the weir (m), and n is the number of side contractions.

free and saline ammonia. *See* **ammonia.**

free chlorine. *See* **residual chlorine.**

freeboard. The vertical distance between the maximum water level in a tank and the top of the side walls, provided to prevent the contents of the tank from being blown over the walls in a high wind. Also the clearance between the periphery of a surface aerator and the static water surface.

freezing process. *See* **sludge freezing process.**

friction coefficient. *See* **coefficient of friction.**

friction head. *See* **head.**

friction loss. Energy lost by friction in the suction and delivery pipes of a pump, including losses at bends and other obstructions.

Froude number. A non-dimensional number which characterizes the type of flow in a hydraulic structure when the liquid is subject to the force of gravity and the influence of inertia. Calculated by dividing the square of the mean velocity of flow by the product of the diameter or depth and the acceleration due to gravity.

frozen-image centrifuge. A commercially-available apparatus used to determine the thickening characteristics of sludges. By conducting a series of tests at a range of centrifugal accelerations, the ultimate concentration expected from a thickener, operated at a range of sludge blanket depths can be predicted.

full-way centrifugal pump. *See* **centrifugal pump.**

fungus. A taxonomic group of spore-producing heterotrophic organisms, most of which are filamentous and often called 'moulds'. Several species are common in biological filters, where they may cause ponding.

Fusarium aquaeductum. A common biological-filter fungus having sickle-shaped spores and often having a pink coloration.

G

galvanizing. Coating the surface of iron with a thin layer of zinc to protect it from oxidation. The following processes are involved: (a) the iron may be annealed to soften it; (b) pickled in hydrochloric or sulphuric acid to remove scale; (c) iron is washed; (d) dipped into a bath of molten zinc to which a flux such as ammonium chloride has been added. Wastewaters include pickling liquor and washwater.

gamma-ray detector. A device which responds to gamma radiation from a suitable source. It can for example be installed in a pipeline conveying sludge from a sedimentation tank which closes an electrically-operated valve and stops the flow of sludge when its density has fallen to a certain level. A source head, supplied with a caesium-137 source, is clamped to the pipe. Gamma rays pass through the sludge and are absorbed in proportion to its density. Rays reaching the detector produce a current which is inversely related to the density. The detector chamber is heated and thermostatically controlled to eliminate temperature variation and moisture condensation.

Gammarus pulex. A freshwater shrimp which may be common in streams and is a useful indicator organism.

Gammexane. *See* **benzene hexachloride**.

garbage. That fraction of municipal refuse comprising solid wastes from the preparation, cooking and dispensing of food; also from the handling, storage and sale of produce.

garbage grinder. *See* **waste disposal unit**.

gas. *See* **sludge gas**.

gas boiler. A boiler in which water is heated by the burning of gas, for example sludge gas. *See* **gas-fired water heater**.

gas chromatography. Chromatography where the mobile phase (or carrier) is a gas. *See* **chromatography**.

gas chromatography-mass spectrometry (GC-MS). A coupled analytical technique using mass spectrometry to identify specific molecules separated from complex mixtures by gas chromatography. The technique allows the routine detection of low levels (0.1 μg/l) of, for example, pesticides. *See* **liquid chromatography – mass spectrometry**.

gas detector. An instrument incorporating a Wheatstone bridge circuit, used for detecting the presence of methane, based on the principle that the combustion of methane on a filament raises the temperature and hence the resistance of the filament, causing 'out of balance' current to flow in the circuit of which it forms part. The current is then displayed either directly, or after amplification, on a meter. Gas detectors may be portable or fixed. Portable detectors also indicate a shortage of oxygen and may have means for detecting hydrogen sulphide.

gas dome. *See* **cover**.

gas-fired water heater. A heater fired by sludge gas, through which water is passed to transfer heat to heat exchangers for heating the contents of primary sludge digestion tanks.

gas-holder. A tank with a floating cover used for storing gas from a sludge digestion plant, for the purposes of (a) stabilizing the flow of gas to the burners; (b) maintaining a nearly constant pressure; and (c) supplying gas during periods when gas production is low.

gas-lift pump. In the context of sludge treatment, a pump which is installed adjacent to a primary digestion tank and uses sludge gas drawn from under the cover for pumping the sludge to achieve mixing and circulation of the contents of the tank and for controlling scum formation.

gas-liquid chromatography (GLC). This employs as the stationary phase a non-volatile liquid supported on an inert solid column packing. GLC can be used for the separation and identification of volatile organic compounds. The retention period for any compound in the chromatographic column under standard conditions, e.g. carrier gas flow rate, temperature, and nature of the stationary phase, is characteristic of that compound. *See* **chromatography**.

gas liquor. Refers to either the concentrated ammoniacal liquor or the spent liquor from a gas works.

gas recirculation. The use of sludge gas for mixing the contents of a primary sludge digestion tank.

gas-works wastes. Gas-works wastewaters include coke-quenching water, wastewaters produced during the manufacture of coal gas, gas-holder over-flow water, and waste liquors from producer and water gas plants.

gate valve. A valve which controls the flow of liquid in a pipe by a plate at right angles to the flow. The plate slides in its own plane and beds on a seating round the bore of the pipe when it is closed. When fully open the full bore of the pipe is available for flow. Also termed a 'screwdown valve', or 'sluice valve'.

Geiger counter. A device for measuring the intensity of ionizing radiation, consisting of a Geiger-Muller tube and electronic equipment for recording the number of ionizations occurring in the tube.

Geotrichum. A fungus commonly occurring on biological filters.

Giardia. *Giardia intestinalis (lamblia)* is a protozoan parasite capable of infecting man and domestic animals. It causes acute diarrhoeal illness.

Glossiphonia. A genus of leeches common in freshwater streams, useful as indicator organisms.

glue and size manufacture. These substances are extracted from bone, skin, horn and hoof by boiling with water, the following processes being involved: (a) skins and hides as received from the tannery steeped in weak hydrochloric acid to remove lime; (b) horns and bones also steeped in weak hydrochloric acid to extract calcium phosphate; (c) cleansed materials boiled with water in vats and fats skimmed off; (d) after prolonged boiling, the liquor is concentrated in vacuum pans to produce cakes of glue on cooling; (e) residue dried and made into manure. Wastewaters include water used for washing raw materials, waste liquor from extraction of lime, occasional discharges of spent lye when soap is being made from fats, and washwater.

Gooch crucible. A crucible, usually of porcelain or silica, with a flat circular perforated base containing a prepared bed of asbestos or other fibres, or a disk of glass fibre paper, through which liquid is withdrawn under a reduced pressure, e.g. when determining the concentration of suspended solids in a sample of domestic or industrial wastewater or treated effluent. After washing the deposit several times with distilled water it is dried until the weight is constant, after which it is ignited to determine its content of volatile matter. Little used technique. *See* **suspended solids**.

grab sample. 1. A sample taken at no set time or rate of flow; also termed a 'spot sample'. 2. A sample of benthos taken by the use of a grab.

gradient. The degree of inclination from the horizontal, expressed as a ratio, percentage, a decimal or in degrees, as for example, the fall of a sewer.

grains per gallon. Used at one time for expressing the concentration of impurities in a wastewater or effluent. Replaced by 'parts per 100 000', then 'parts per million', and finally by 'milligrammes per litre' or 'milligrammes per kilogramme'. 1 grain equals 1/7000 of a pound Avoirdupois, or grains per gallon x 14.3 = mg/1.

grassland irrigation. *See* **irrigation over grassland**.

grass-plot treatment. *See* **irrigation over grassland**.

gravimetric. Pertaining to measurement by weight, as with quantitative chemical analysis based on the weight of reactants and products of reaction.

grazing fauna. When referring to biological filters, the insects, worms and other invertebrates which graze on the microbial film and thereby prevent its continued accumulation.

grease. In sewage treatment, grease includes fats, oils, waxes, free fatty acids, calcium and magnesium soaps, mineral oils, and other non-fatty materials. The type of solvent used for its extraction should be stated.

grease trap. A receptacle designed to collect and retain grease and fatty substances in kitchen wastes or in an industrial wastewater and installed in the drainage system between the point of production and the sewer.

green liquor. When pulp is being manufactured from wood, the liquor containing the ash of the spent lye from the digesters after incineration.

Grey List. A list of substances hazardous in the water environment. The basis of legislation for the elimination or reduction of pollution of inland and coastal waters is the Dangerous Substances Directive (76/464/EEC). This and other Directives and Conventions list substances considered to be hazardous, and which must be eliminated or controlled. The Grey List (sometimes referred to as List 2) contains substances that are less harmful than Red List (cf.) substances.

grey sour. Treatment of cotton goods with a weak acid after the 'lime boil' prior to bleaching. Also termed 'first sour'.

grey washing. First washing of cotton goods with water prior to bleaching.

grey water. Drainage from domestic washing and food preparation. cf. **black water**.

grit. The heavy mineral matter in sewage, such as silt,sand, gravel, cinders, ashes, metal and glass. It is abrasive in character and may vary in composition seasonally. Soil originating from vegetable washing and preparation is also classified as grit.

grit channel. *See* **constant-velocity grit channel**.

grit dredger. A machine for removing grit from a grit channel or tank, originally consisting of a pair of endless chains running on sprocket wheels and carrying a series of buckets reaching down into the grit and lifting it for discharge into a screw conveyor or on to a belt conveyor.

grit washer. A device for washing grit to remove organic matter.

growth constant. The rate of multiplication, expressed as the rate of increase in population per unit population present. In the activated-sludge process, the mass of sludge wasted per day divided by the mass of sludge in the aeration tank.

H

habitat. A place where a biological species lives.

half-life. The time taken for half the atoms in a radioactive isotope to disintegrate. Half-lives vary from isotope to isotope, from millionths of a second to more than a million years.

hard detergent. A synthetic detergent which is resistant to biological oxidation, and less than 90 per cent is removed in normal sewage treatment. An example is tetrapropylene benzene sulphonate.

hardness. A characteristic of water due to the presence of compounds of calcium, magnesium and iron dissolved in it. When soap is used, instead of the water forming an immediate lather, the fatty acids of the soap combine with the salts of the metals to form an insoluble scum. Hardness causes increased consumption of soap. It also causes (a) deposition of scale in boilers; (b) injurious effects in some industrial processes; and (c) sometimes objectionable taste in water. It is commonly determined by EDTA titration. *See* **permanent hardness, temporary hardness**.

Hazen number. A number used to define the colour of water, the standard unit being the colour produced by 1 milligramme of platinum per litre (in the form of chloroplatinic acid) in the presence of 2 milligrammes of cobaltous chloride hexahydrate per litre.

Hazen's Theory. A theory concerning the settlement of granular particles, proposed by A. Hazen in the USA in 1904. He found that as the size of particles increased there was a transition stage during which the viscosity of the fluid became less important and the importance of fluid friction increased. He showed mathematically that surface loading was the most important factor in the design of sedimentation tanks.

head. The total head against which a pump is to deliver is made up of the static head, plus friction head, plus velocity head. The static head is the actual lift, from the minimum level of the liquid in the wet well to the point of discharge. The friction head is the energy lost by friction in the suction and delivery pipes, including losses at bends and obstructions. The velocity head is the energy per unit weight of liquid being pumped due to its velocity.

heat exchanger. A unit in which a liquid at a relatively low temperature circulates in passages (or conduits) surrounded by a liquid at a higher temperature, or vice versa, so that heat is transferred from one liquid to the other.

heat treatment. A process introduced by N. Testrup in 1911 and subsequently improved by W. K. Porteous for conditioning sludge prior to dewatering, based on heating it under pressure to about 180°C and maintaining it at an elevated temperature, usually from 180° to 200°C, for up to an hour to break down the gel structure. After pre-heating using heat from treated sludge, it is heated further by injecting steam or indirectly using pressurized hot water or hot air. Sometimes termed 'high-temperature treatment'. It is now obsolete in the UK. *See* **wet-air oxidation**.

heat-treatment liquor. Liquor separated from sludge by decantation or filtration after the sludge has been heated under pressure and maintained at an elevated temperature, usually from 180° to 200°C, for up to an hour. It has a very high BOD and COD and a strong characteristic odour.

heavy metals. Metals such as copper, zinc, cadmium, nickel and lead, which are commonly used in industry and which can, if present in sufficiently high concentration, retard or inhibit aerobic and anaerobic biological processes and be harmful to living organisms.

Helobdella stagnalis. A species of leech, useful as an indicator organism.

Hemiptera. Bugs, which are a class of insects having mouth parts modified for piercing and sucking fluids of plants or animals. Several species are aquatic, e.g. water boatman.

herringbone system. A system of drainage for land or a sludge drying bed in which sub-drains, usually consisting of agricultural pipes, are laid in parallel lines at an angle to the main drain and slope towards it.

heterotrophes. Organisms which require organic matter as a source of energy, being incapable of synthesizing their own from inorganic sources, cf. **autotrophic bacteria**.

high-intensity cone aerator. *See* **cone aerator**.

high-pressure (or performance) liquid chromatography (HPLC). Chromatography where the mobile phase (or carrier) is a liquid under pressure. *See* **chromatography**.

high-rate activated-sludge process. A modification of the activated-sludge process whereby a much shorter aeration period than usual and possibly a high mixed-liquor suspended-solids concentration are used. *See* **high-rate treatment**.

high-rate filter. A biological filter containing a coarse medium or a synthetic medium operating with a hydraulic loading exceeding 3 cubic metres per cubic metre per day, or an organic loading exceeding 2 kilogrammes of BOD per cubic metre per day.

high-rate treatment. Any plant which is operated purposely at a hydraulic or organic loading significantly greater than that usually employed, without special regard to the quality of the effluent which the plant produces, or to the type of wastewater being treated

high-temperature treatment. *See* **heat treatment**.

hindered settling. *See* **rate of hindered settling**.

Hirudinea. Leeches, several species of which occur in rivers and are of value as indicator organisms.

holophytic. Plant-like nutrition; obtaining food by photosynthesis.

holozoic. Animal-like nutrition; obtaining their food as particulate organic matter, living or freshly killed. cf. **saprozoic**.

homeostasis. The maintenance of an equilibrium in a biological system; physiologically, the constancy of the internal environment of an organism or ecologically the balance of a community of organisms with the external environment.

homeostatic control. The maintenance of homeostasis. *See* **homeostasis**.

hook gauge. A pointed, U-shaped hook attached to a vernier which can be moved along a graduated staff, usually by means of a screw. The hook is lowered to a point below the water surface and then raised until this is just pierced, indicated by the appearance of a pimple on the surface. Used for accurately measuring the elevation of a water surface.

hookworm. Nematodes having mouth parts armed with hooks. In the adult stage they are parasitic on mammals, including man, attaching themselves to the wall of the intestine.

horizontal-flow sand filter. A sand filter in which the flow is either radial (Simater filter) or from one side of a bed of sand to the other (Bohna filter). With the Simater filter a mixture of sand and effluent is pumped continuously from below the filter to the top by an air-lift pump, sludge in the sand being removed by elutriation. With the Bohna filter, effluent is used for back-washing by gravity flow.

horizontal-flow tank. A rectangular tank with the inlet at one end and the outlet usually consisting of a weir spanning the tank at the other end, the floor sloping towards a sludge draw-off at the inlet end.

humus. Ecologically, the biologically stabilized dead organic material resulting from aerobic decomposition of plant and animal material and their waste products. *See* **humus sludge**.

humus sludge. Sludge which is voided by biological filters and settles in secondary settlement tanks. *See* **humus**.

humus tank. *See* **secondary settlement tanks**.

Hydracarina. Water mites, which are a family of the class Arachnida, common in freshwater habitats. Most are highly coloured, unlike other freshwater organisms.

hydrated lime. Limestone which has been 'burned' and treated with water under controlled conditions until its content of calcium oxide has been converted to calcium hydroxide.

hydraulic gradient. The loss of head in a liquid flowing in a pipe or channel, expressed as a ratio, the slope of a curve, or as a fractional drop (m/km). When the liquid is flowing under pressure in a pipeline, it is the slope of the line joining the elevations to which the liquid would rise in pipes freely vented and under atmospheric pressure. With a channel or sewer, it is the slope of the free surface of the flowing liquid.

hydraulic jump. An abrupt rise in water surface which may occur in an open channel when the water flowing at a high velocity is retarded, as with the standing-wave which occurs immediately downstream of a measuring flume.

hydraulic loading. The volumetric loading rate. As applied to a biological filter, it is the rate of application expressed in cubic metres of sewage per cubic metre of medium per day.

hydraulic mean depth. With water flowing in an open channel, the cross-sectional area of the stream divided by the wetted perimeter of the channel. Also termed 'hydraulic radius'.

hydraulic radius. *See* **hydraulic mean depth**.

Hydrobaenus. A genus of chironomid midge, an active grazer in some biological filters. Also termed *'Spaniotoma'*.

hydrobiology. The biology of aquatic organisms.

hydrodynamics. The branch of hydraulics which deals with flow over weirs, and through openings, pipes and channels.

hydrogen-ion concentration. *See* **pH value**.

hydrological survey. A comprehensive survey in a river basin of rainfall, run off, evaporation, ground water, public and private sources of supply, effluent discharges, reuse of water, and the yield from controlled catchments (existing and potential) to produce a balance sheet of resources and requirements.

hydrometric scheme. A scheme for obtaining and recording measurements and other particulars of: (a) rainfall in an area; (b) the evaporation of water in that area; (c) the flow, level, or volume of inland waters in the area, other than inland waters falling within section 2(3) of the Water Resources Act 1963; and (d) other matters appearing to the authority to affect, or to be likely to affect water resources in the area.

hydrometry. The measurement and analysis of the flow of water.

hydrophobic colloid. Finely-divided particles which, when suspended in water, precipitate readily.

Hydropsyche. A genus of Trichoptera or caddis-flies. In their larval stages they do not build cases like most caddis but catch their food in nets which they spin in flowing water. Useful indicator organisms.

hydrostatic head. A pressure differential created by a difference in liquid levels.

hydrostatic presure. The pressure at any point in a liquid at rest. Equal to the depth of liquid above the point multiplied by its density. When withdrawing sludge from a tank under hydrostatic pressure the point of withdrawal is lower than the surface of the water in the tank.

hypha. A cellular filament of a fungus.

Hypogastrura viatica. A species of the primitive insect order Collembola, characterized by having a simple life cycle and by not having wings. A common member of the grazing fauna of many biological filters. Also termed *'Achorutes subviaticus'*.

hypolimnion. The lowermost layer of a stratified body of water, i.e. that below the thermocline.

I

Imhoff cone. A graduated glass cone, usually of 1 litre capacity, used in the laboratory for measuring the proportion of settleable solids in a sewage or effluent.

Imhoff tank. A deep two-storied tank introduced in Germany by Karl Imhoff in 1906 and formerly much used in Germany and the USA. It consists of an upper or continuous-flow sedimentation chamber and a lower sludge-digestion chamber. The floor of the upper chamber slopes steeply to trapped slots through which solids may slide into the lower chamber. The lower chamber receives no fresh sewage directly, but is provided with gas vents and with means for withdrawing digested sludge from near the bottom.

Immedium sand filter. *See* **upward-flow sand filter**.

impeller. The rotating portion of a pump, blower or fan, with backward curved vanes, a central inlet and a peripheral outlet. When rotating at a high speed, centrifugal force causes liquid or air to be discharged from the periphery in a continuous stream and a partial vacuum to be created at the centre so that further liquid or air is drawn in.

impermeability factor. The ratio of the amount of water which runs off a surface to that which falls on it, e.g. watertight roof surfaces, 0.70–0.95: macadam road, 0.25–0.60; gravel road, 0.15–0.30; parks 0.05–0.30; woodland, 0.01–0.20.

impervious area. An area through which water cannot percolate, e.g. roads, roofs of houses, yards, and therefore the amount of water running off the area is equal to the amount of water falling on it.

incineration. As applied to sewage treatment, the burning of screenings or sewage sludge to produce an ash which may be innocuous depending on its heavy metal content.

inclined plate separator. *See* **laminar flow separation**.

incremental loading. *See* **stepped feeding**.

incubator test. *See* **stability test**.

indicator organisms. Organisms which, by their presence or absence, indicate the condition or degree of pollution of an aquatic habitat, e.g. (a) the types of protozoa in an activated-sludge plant; (b) algae and aquatic invertebrates in a body of water.

industrial alcohol. Industrial alcohol may be made from molasses or synthetically from petroleum feed-stocks. When made from molasses, varying proportions of malt and grain are added and the molasses then passes through the following processes: (a) dilution with hot water, or mixture sterilised by heating; (b) mixture settled and yeast added to liquor; (c) sulphuric acid and nutrients added and alkali neutralized; (d) 'mash' fermented in stages; (e) liquor distilled to recover alcohol. Residue from distillation is known as 'molasses slop'. Wastewaters include steep water, liquor from distillation, and washwaters.

industrial river. A river whose function has become primarily that of a carrier of effluents from domestic and industrial wastewater treatment plants which form a large proportion of the flow in dry weather.

industrial sewage. *See* **sewage**.

industrial wastewater. *See* **trade effluent**.

infiltration water. Ground water entering a drain or sewer through broken or porous pipes, or through defective joints.

influent. Water, sewage or other liquid, untreated or partially treated, flowing into a section of the treatment plant.

initial interface velocity. *See* **rate of hindered settling**.

initial settling rate. *See* **rate of hindered settling**.

injector tine. A plough-like device which penetrates and lifts the soil to allow sludge to be injected below the surface.

Inka process. A development of the activated-sludge process which originated in Sweden about 1958 and was introduced into the UK about 1961. Bubbles of air are introduced into the aeration tank from pipes with orifices on the underside, located at a depth less than half that of the tank. A submerged vertical baffle extends throughout the length of the tank but space is left between the baffle and the tank floor so that, with the air being introduced on one side of the baffle, the mixed liquor assumes a spiral flow during its passage through the tank.

inland water. Comprises (a) any river, stream or other watercourse, whether natural or artificial and whether tidal or not; (b) any lake or pond whether natural or artificial, and any reservoir or dock; (c) any channel, creek, bay, estuary or arm of the sea, so long as it is within any of the National River Authority (England and Wales) or River Purification Board (Scotland) areas.

inorganic matter. Matter which, in general, does not contain organic carbon atoms except as carbonates, carbides, etc.

inspection chamber. 1. A chamber on a sewer, e.g. at the junction of a house drain with the sewer. 2. Under the Public Health Act 1961, a local authority may direct that industrial wastewater discharged from trade premises into the public sewer shall pass through an inspection chamber from which samples of the wastewater may readily be taken. 3. A chamber into which sludge discharges from a sedimentation tank through a telescopic bellmouth or other outlet; permits visual inspection of the sludge being discharged.

INSTAB. Information Service on Toxicity and Biodegradability, introduced by the Water Pollution Research Laboratory in 1966 to supply any information available on the behaviour of individual materials in aerobic and anaerobic biological processes, and on their toxicity to fish and other aquatic organisms. This information service has been continued by the Water Research Centre with considerable expansion on toxicology.

integrator. A device which indicates the total volume of liquid or gas which has passed over or through a measuring device, or which summates the hours run by operating units or the number of operations carried out.

intercepting sewer. A sewer which receives sewage from a number of transverse sewers or outlets.

interceptor. A trap designed to intercept, separate and prevent the passage of oil, fats and grease, or of sand, present in sewage or surface water.

intermittent downward filtration (land). A system, now almost obsolete in the UK, in which land was used exclusively or mainly for the treatment of sewage. The land areas were underdrained and either surrounded by low earth banks or laid out in a series of ridges and furrows so that sewage could be applied every few days, with longer periods of rest at intervals to enable the land to be cultivated. With ridge and furrow irrigation, crops were grown on the ridges. Also termed 'flood irrigation'.

International Organization for Standardization (ISO). An international organization founded in 1946 which aims to promote the development of standards in the world with a view to facilitating the international exchange of goods and services and to developing mutual co-operation in the sphere of intellectual, scientific, technological, and economic activity. Its publications are in English, French and Russian, and it is represented in the UK by the British Standards Institution. *See* **British Standards Institution**.

International System of Units (SI). Or the Système International des Unités, a modified and simplified form of the metric system, approved internationally in 1960 and to which the UK has changed. It rationalizes the main metric units of measurement and standardizes their names and symbolic representation. The system is based on seven units, the metre (m) as the unit of length, the kilogramme (kg) as the unit of mass, the second (s) as the unit of time, the ampere (A) as the unit of electric current, the degree kelvin ($°K$) as the unit of temperature, the candela (cd) as the unit of luminous intensity, and the mole (mol) as the unit of substance amount.

invert. The lowest point on the internal surface of a drain, sewer or channel.

invertebrates. Animals not possessing a backbone.

inverted siphon. A section of sewer constructed lower than adjacent sections to pass beneath a valley, watercourse or other obstruction. It always runs full if the soffit is lower than the inverts of the adjacent sections.

ion. An electrically charged atom or group of atoms having either an excess or a deficiency of electrons the migration of which effects the passage of electricity through an electrolyte.

ion-exchange process. The reversible exchange of ions between a solid and a liquid or between two immiscible liquids. For example, calcium ions (hardness) in water can be exchanged for sodium ions from a cation-exchange resin as a softening process. *See* **deionization**.

ion selective electrode. A device that develops an electrical potential proportional to the logarithm of the activity of a particular ion, towards which it has been designed to exhibit a high degree of selectivity over other ions which may be present in the sample. The four main types are (a) glass electrodes of the pH type which, by incorporating special glasses can be made selective to H^+, Na^+, K^+, Ag^+, NH_4^+ Li^+, and Cs^+; (b) electrodes with single crystal or pressed crystalline disk membranes, e.g. the lanthanum fluoride crystal used in the fluoride electrode; (c) heterogeneous electrodes in which the active constituent is dispersed in an inert binder; (d) liquid ion-exchange membrane electrodes in which an inert hydrophobic porous disk forms the interface between the internal ion-exchange liquid and the sample, while a third solution maintains a constant activity of the appropriate ion within the electrode.

iron and steel industry wastes. Wastewaters from the iron and steel industry include large volumes of water used for cooling purposes and gas washing in the manufacture of pig iron, water used for cooling and quenching, rinse waters, and pickling liquors.

iron bacteria. Bacteria of the order Chlamydobacteriales which exhibit the capacity to abstract iron from ferruginous waters and deposit it in their sheaths. Some *(Crenothrix, Gallionella, Leptothrix)* are claimed to be capable of metabolically oxidizing ferrous salts to ferric salts autotrophically. In others *(Sphaerotilus)* it has been shown that this oxidation is purely chemical and takes place in the sheath of the bacterium.

irradiation. Exposure of a liquid or sludge to intensive radiation from a radio-active source or source of high-energy electrons in order to destroy pathogenic organisms .

irrigation. The application of sewage or an effluent to land, by flooding, the use of furrows, or by spraying.

irrigation over grassland. A method of removing finely-divided suspended matter from biologically-treated sewage by permitting the sewage to flow over grassland. The grassland is divided into plots which are used alternately for treatment and then rested and renovated.

isoelectric point. The pH value at which the charge on a colloidal particle is zero.

isoproturon. A herbicide belonging to the urea group.

isotopes. Atoms of the same chemical element with the same atomic number but different atomic weights, i.e. the nuclei have the same number of protons but different numbers of neutrons.

J

Jet aeration. A trade name for a system of aeration used in the activated-sludge process in which coarse bubbles of air are introduced under a relatively low pressure through orifices in pipes immersed at a depth of less than one-third of the depth of the aeration tank.

Jeta grit trap. Formerly known as the Pista grit trap (cf.), its principle difference is an impeller designed to produce an upward spiral flow around the centre to carry lighter sewage solids to the surface with grit settling in the hopper.

jetting machine. A machine using high-pressure water for cleansing purposes.

K

katabolism. Conversion by living organisms of complex organic molecules into simpler ones, resulting in the release of energy.

Kenics aerator. A trade name for a proprietary type of spiral-tube aerator.

Kessener brush aerator. *See* **brush aerator**.

kier liquor. The waste produced when vegetable matter is boiled in a solution of caustic soda to release the fibres, usually carried out under pressure, e.g. before bleaching of cotton yarn.

kiering. Boiling of cotton yarn or fabric in an alkaline solution, usually under pressure. The vessel in which the operation takes place is called a 'kier'.

Kjeldahl nitrogen. The total organic nitrogen in a sewage or effluent estimated by the Kjeldahl process, based on conversion of the nitrogen to ammonium sulphate and distillation of the ammonia after the solution has been made alkaline. The ammonia which distils over is a measure of the Kjeldahl nitrogen.

Kolkwitz-Marsson saprobic system. *See* **saprobien system**.

Kraus process. A 'remedy' proposed by L.S. Kraus in the USA in 1945 for overloading of an activated-sludge plant and consequent sludge 'bulking'. A mixture of digestion tank supernatant liquor, digested sludge and activated sludge was aerated in a special tank and then added to the returned activated sludge in order (a) to control the sludge density index and thus prevent bulking, and (b) to provide nitrate as a supplementary source of oxygen.

L

lag phase of growth. The phase of growth of a microbial culture in which the organism conditions itself to a new environment and the rate of multiplication is slower than in the logarithmic phase which follows.

lagoon. An artificial lake constructed by excavation and using the excavated soil for forming embankments, or employing a natural depression. Used for storing and consolidating sludge or, where land is cheap and the climate is suitable, for stabilizing organic matter in crude or biologically-treated sewage by providing a relatively long period of retention.

lamella separator. Parallel plates within a settlement tank which greatly increases the settling surface so reducing the size of tank needed. Each plate acts as a very shallow settling tank in which the solids have only a short vertical distance to fall. They have been widely used for industrial applications and drinking water treatment, and have been applied to sewage treatment in Europe since the mid-1980's, although usually with the addition of a settlement aid. Lamella plates are installed as modules at an angle of 55° to the horizontal and the sewage is introduced from below. Solid matter settles on the inclined plates and slides downwards against the upward flow of the sewage.

laminar flow. Smooth, although not necessarily uniform, flow in which the liquid can be regarded as moving in parallel layers each of which has a constant velocity, there being no mixing between adjoining layers.

laminar flow separation. A process developed in Sweden for removing suspended solids from a liquid by passing the liquid through a sloping multi-floor 'separator' in which the solids settle only a short distance before reaching the floor, down which they slide into a separating tank.

laminar velocity. *See* **critical velocity**.

land treatment. The treatment of settled sewage on land by broad irrigation, intermittent downward filtration, spray irrigation or sub-surface irrigation. *See* **broad irrigation, intermittent downward filtration, spray irrigation, sub-surface irrigation**.

landfill. The engineered deposit of waste onto and into land in such a manner that pollution or harm to the environment is prevented and, through restoration, land is provided which may be used for another purpose. *See* **co-disposal**.

landfill leachate. The liquors which drain from the base of a landfill site. For domestic landfill they are characterized by high concentrations of BOD and COD.

Langelier index. The difference between the actual pH value of a water and its saturation pH value, the latter being the value at which water of the same alkalinity and calcium hardness would be in equilibrium with excess calcium carbonate at the same temperature and content of dissolved solids. Waters with a positive Langelier Index are supersaturated with calcium carbonate and will tend to deposit it as a scale. Waters with a negative Langelier Index are undersaturated with calcium carbonate and will tend to be aggressive and dissolve chalk. The saturation pH can be determined by calculation or from nomographs.

larva. A pre-adult development stage of an insect in which feeding is independent of the parent.

LAS. Abbreviation for linear alkyl benzene sulphonate; these are biologically 'soft' surfactants.

lateral sewer. A sewer which has no tributary sewers and discharges into a branch or other sewer.

laundry wastes. In commercial laundering the soiled fabrics are washed, boiled and rinsed in machines, chemical substances being added the most important of which are detergent or soap, sodium carbonate and a bleaching agent. Wastewaters include washwaters and rinsing waters.

LC 50 value. *See* **lethal concentration**.

leach liquor. The first water to be run off after flax has been steeped in water for several hours in a retting tank.

leaping weir overflow. An overflow whereby dry-weather sewage is discharged to the downstream foul sewer through an opening in the floor of the chamber. Storm flows 'leap' across the opening and are discharged by another outlet.

leather dressing. Process by which tanned or partially tanned skins and hides are worked up into light leather for the 'uppers' of boots and shoes including re-tanning, dyeing and finishing.

Legionella. Organisms of the genus *Legionella* are classified as Gram-negative bacteria of which there are at least 30 species, over half of which have been implicated in human disease. *L. pneumophila* is the causative agent of Legionnaires' disease, an acute pneumonic infection of the lungs, and greater than 85% of cases are caused by *L. pneumophila* serogroup 1.

Leptomitus lacteus. A non-septate aquatic fungus found in certain organically enriched waters.

Leptospira icterohaemorrhagiae. A pathogenic spirochaete which may invade the blood causing leptospiral jaundice (Weil's disease), transmitted by sewer rats and their urine.

Leptothrix. A filamentous genus of the iron bacteria, Chlamydobacteriaceae, found in organically polluted waters.

lethal concentration (LC 50 value). The concentration of a toxic substance which kills one half of a group of test animals in a given period, e.g. 48-hour LC 50.

Leuctra. A genus of Plecoptera (stone-flies) having aquatic nymphs in flowing waters; indicative of well-aerated water.

level-sensing device. A device for automatically controlling the operation of a centrifugal pump, depending on the level in the wet well, or for recording the volume of sludge or chemical in a storage tank. Such devices include conductivity or capacitance electrodes, pneumatic tubes or cells, float-mounted relays, ultrasonics, gamma rays, or float systems.

lime boil. Boiling cotton goods with milk of lime in a kier prior to bleaching.

limeyard wastes. *See* **beam-house wastes**.

limit of detection (LOD). The lowest concentration of a determinand that can be reported arising from the analysis of a given matrix by a given analytical technique. Statistical techniques can be used to ensure that a true response is reported and not an abnormally high 'blank'.

Limnaea. A genus of freshwater snail commonly found in fresh waters and tolerant of a wide range of conditions.

limnology. The study of the physical, chemical and biological aspects of inland waters.

linear alkyl benzene sulphonate (LAS). The biodegradable or 'soft' anionic surfactant which replaced ABS as the major surfactant component of household synthetic detergents in Britain.

linear settling rate. *See* **rate of hindered settling**.

liquefaction. Changing of organic matter from an insoluble to a soluble state, thereby effecting a reduction in the suspended solids content of the liquid.

liquid chromatography-mass spectrometry (LC-MS). A coupled analytical technique using mass spectrometry to identify specific molecules separated from complex mixtures by liquid chromatography. The technique allows the routine detection of low levels (0.1 µg/l) of temperature sensitive molecules such as atrazine. *See* **gas chromatography-mass spectrometry**.

liquid sludge. Sludge which is sufficiently dilute to enable it to flow by gravity or be pumped.

liquor. 1. Water containing matter in solution and suspension, such as that which separates from sludge after digestion or during dewatering. 2. An industrial wastewater having a high BOD and/or containing a high concentration of suspended solids. *See* **ammoniacal liquor, black liquor, condenser liquor, dephenolated gas liquor, gas liquor, green liquor, heat-treatment liquor, leach liquor, mixed liquor, retort-house liquor, scrubber liquor, spent liquor, supernatant liquor**.

lithium chloride. *See* **chemical tracer**.

lithophilous. Living on or amongst rocks or stones.

Litonotus. Or *Lionotus*, a genus of free swimming ciliate protozoa common in activated sludge.

littoral zone. The shallow marginal zone of a body of water where light penetrates to the bottom. Usually colonized by rooted vegetation.

load unit. An expression used in South Africa for denoting the load on a biological filter, calculated by multiplying the permanganate value of the settled sewage by the hydraulic loading in terms of cubic metres per cubic metre of medium per day.

local authority. In England and Wales, a county council or district council, metropolitan district council, or London borough council. In Scotland, a regional council, islands council, or a district council.

log phase of growth. The phase of growth of a microbial culture when the growth rate is maximal under the particular conditions and is logarithmic i.e. the population doubles in equal intervals of time.

loss on ignition. In sewage analysis, the percentage loss in weight of the suspended solids retained on a glass fibre or asbestos pad after filtration of a sample when ignited at 600°C .

low wines. In the manufacture of whisky, the distillate from distillation of the 'wort'.

lower explosive limit. *See* **explosive limits**.

Lumbricillus. Or *Pachydrilus*, a genus of the family Enchytraeidae. Small worms of a pale colour which are common grazers in biological filters.

Lumbricus. A genus of worm of the family Lumbricidae, which includes the common earth worm. Other species are grazers in biological filters.

lye boil. Boiling of cotton goods under pressure in a solution of soda ash and resin soap before bleaching.

lyophilic colloid. A colloid which is readily dispersed in a suitable medium and attracts that medium.

lyophobic colloid. A colloid which has no attraction for the medium in which it is dispersed and therefore tends to separate from the medium.

M

macerator. Often incorrectly used instead of the term 'disintegrator'. *See* **screenings disintegrator**.

McGowan strength. A method of assessing the strength of sewage, suggested by Dr G. McGowan in the Fifth Report of the Royal Commission on Sewage Disposal (1908), but now virtually obsolete in the UK, using the following formula:

Strength = (ammoniacal nitrogen + organic nitrogen) x 4.5
+ (N/8 permanganate value x 6.5),

all values being expressed in mg/1 (since it is sometimes expressed in parts per 100 000, the method of expression should be clearly stated).

A modern form of the formula is:

Strength = (Total N × 4.5) + (N/8 PV × 6.5)mg/1.

The factor 6.5 relates to domestic sewage; for an industrial wastewater a different factor, e.g. ultimate carbonaceous BOD divided by N/8PV, needs to be used.

Mackereth dissolved-oxygen electrode. An electrode patented by F.J.H. Mackereth in 1962 and used in the measurement and recording of dissolved oxygen. *See* **dissolved-oxygen electrode**.

macrophytes. Plants other than algae, mosses and liverworts. Some large algae, such as *Cladophora*, are often referred to as macrophytic.

magma. Term used for the greasy sludge produced by the acid cracking of wool-scouring liquor.

magma filter. In acid cracking of wool-scouring liquor, an open bed similar to a sludge-drying bed on to which the sludge containing the grease is run so that the liquid can drain from it.

magnetic flow meter. A meter which can be installed in a pipeline for measuring flows, based on the principle that the voltage induced in a conductor of known length and moving through a magnetic field set up inside the pipe between electrical probes is proportional to the velocity of that conductor, and hence to the rate of flow, since the conductor is in this case the fluid. It can also measure the flow when this is in the opposite direction.

malting. The preparation of barley for use in brewing, involving the following processes: (a) barley steeped or soaked in water which is either renewed several times or flows continuously through the tank in which the steeping takes place; (b) wet grain spread on floor to germinate, or allowed to germinate in a rotating drum, under controlled conditions of temperature, moisture and aeration; (c) grain slowly dried in a kiln; (d) treated mechanically to remove rootlets. Wastewaters include steep water and washwaters.

Mammoth rotor. A trade name for an aerator used in the activated-sludge process. It is about 1 metre in diameter and consists of a series of blades rotating about a horizontal drive shaft, each blade being in a different plane, arranged so that the blades come into contact with the mixed liquor one at a time.

manhole. 1. An opening by which a person can normally enter or leave a sewer, sump or underground chamber or gain access to a pipeline, for inspection, testing, cleaning or other maintenance operations; closed by a removable cover. 2. A chamber on a drain or sewer providing a means of access.

Manning's formula. A formula expressing the relationship between the average velocity of flow in a channel, the hydraulic mean depth and the hydraulic gradient or slope, thus:

$$V = \frac{1}{N} R^{0.67} S^{0.50}$$

where V is the average velocity of flow (m/s), N is a coefficient of roughness, R is the hydraulic mean depth (m), and S is the hydraulic gradient or slope.

manometer. 1. An instrument used for measuring pressure. Usually consists of a U-tube containing a liquid such as mercury, one limb being connected to the gas or liquid under pressure while the other limb is open to the atmosphere.

The liquid surface in the open limb moves proportionately with changes in pressure of the gas or liquid. 2. An instrument used for measuring differences in pressure, in which case the limbs are connected to the two points between which the pressure difference is to be determined.

manual closed-loop process control. A technique for controlling a continuous-flow process involving (a) the initial setting, (b) a visual indication of the result, (c) assessment of any deviation from the desired result, (d) correction by manual operation to produce the desired result. Control is by manual operation. *See* **process control techniques**.

manure. A natural product which supplies varying amounts of plant nutrients and organic matter to the soil. In addition to the major nutrients, i.e. nitrogen, phosphorus, potassium and magnesium, it contains trace elements needed by plants for healthy growth. The organic content helps to maintain soil stability and humus formed during decomposition helps to retain moisture in the soil. Organic manures include farmyard manure, sewage sludge, and composts made from plant residues or domestic refuse. *See* **fertilizer**.

manure gun. A device used for spraying sludge over an area of land. It has a discharge nozzle about 50 mm in diameter and was originally designed to pass pulverized farm wastes. *See* **rain-gun**.

marine deposits. *See* **benthal deposit**.

mash tun. In brewing, the extraction vessel in which ground malt is steeped in water to enable enzymic changes to take place, of which the conversion of starch to sugar is the most important. The liquid from the mash tun is called 'wort'

mashing. In the manufacture of whisky, the operation of steeping malt in hot water to convert starch to sugar by enzymic action.

mass balance. The quantitative expression of the principle of the conservation of mass as applied to a reaction or process. In its simplest form the mass balance merely states that the total accumulation of mass within a system is equal to the difference between the mass which has entered and that which has been removed. The mass balance may also be drawn for any conservative substance and it is in this form that it often becomes invaluable in the analysis of fairly complex systems, especially if one rate of transfer cannot be measured without difficulty.

mass spectrometry (MS). Separation of ions of differing mass by the action of electrical and magnetic fields and the subsequent measurement of the abundance of the various ionic species revealed by the separation process.

mass-transfer coefficient. The constant of proportionality in an equation relating to the rate of transfer of a particular substance to the effective area available for transfer and the transfer driving force. As an example, consider a soluble substance passing into solution across an interfacial area A; if at time t the concentration already in solution is C the rate of change of the mass m in solution will be directly proportional to the difference between the solubility at equilibrium C_S and the instantaneous concentration C, thus:

$$dm/dt = K_L A (C_S - C)$$

where K_L is the mass-transfer coefficient. When consistent units are used in this equation the mass-transfer coefficient has the dimensions of length per unit time.

maturation pond. A large shallow basin used for the further treatment of sewage which has already received biological treatment and from which the solids synthesized in biological treatment have been removed. *See* **lagoon**.

maximum acceptable (or admissible) concentration (MAC). The maximum average atmospheric concentration of contaminants to which workers may be exposed for an 8-hour working day without injury to health, or the maximum acceptable concentration below which the concentration of a pollutant in water, wastewater and treated effluent must be maintained in order to comply with the requirements of the relevant legislation. For gases and vapours, expressed in terms of parts of vapour or gas per million parts of air, by volume; for toxic dusts, fumes and mists, in milligrammes per cubic metre of air; for mineral dusts, in millions of particles per cubic metre of air. *See* **prescribed concentration value**.

maximum settling rate. *See* **rate of hindered settling**.

mechanical aeration. *See* **surface aeration**.

mechanical flocculation. The use of specially designed stirring mechanisms to promote conditions under which the agglomeration of finely-divided suspended solids can occur, with adsorption of colloidal matter on to the flocs.

median flow in dry weather. The median value of sewage flows on days when rainfall is less than or equal to 1mm for a selected period of time (usually a quarter year).

median tolerance limit (TL_m). The value of a physical factor to which concentration terms do not apply, e.g. temperature, at which half of a batch of test organisms are killed within a specified period.

medium screen. A screen with apertures of 15 to 50mm.

membrane electrode. *See* **dissolved-oxygen electrode**.

membrane filter press. A pressure filter whose filter plates have an inflatable membrane incorporated into them to expel more filtrate from the sludge cake after normal pressure filtration.

mercerizing. Steeping cotton goods in a solution of caustic soda to give them a silky finish, followed by washing with water and finally with a dilute solution of acid. Wastewaters include spent liquor and washwaters.

mesophilic digestion. Anaerobic digestion of sludge at a temperature of approximately 35°C, thereby encouraging the growth of bacteria which grow best at this temperature i.e. mesophilic bacteria.

mesophilic organisms. Those organisms requiring a temperature of approximately 35°C.

mesosaprobic. The intermediate zone of recovery from organic pollution according to the saprobien system.

metabolic respiration. *See* **respiration**.

metabolism. Controlled chemical reactions associated with living organisms. Katabolism is destructive metabolism, in which complex compounds are decomposed into simpler ones, with release of energy which becomes available for the organism's activities. Anabolism is constructive metabolism, in which simpler compounds are built up into more complex ones with the absorption or storage of energy.

metabolite. A chemical substance involved in metabolic activity.

metal processing and finishing. Metal processing and finishing includes electro-plating, anodizing, case-hardening and pickling.

methaemoglobinaemia. A disease of babies caused by drinking nitrate-rich water. In the digestive tract the nitrate is reduced to nitrite which converts haemoglobin to methaemoglobin, causing cyanosis (blueness of the skin).

methane. An inflammable odourless gas CH_4, which is the main constituent of sludge gas.

methane bacteria. Methanogenic bacteria which, in the absence of oxygen, induce an alkaline fermentation of putrescible organic matter and produce methane gas.

methane fermentation. Fermentation during which organic matter is converted into a mixture of methane and carbon dioxide, as during sludge digestion.

methyl orange alkalinity. *See* **alkalinity**.

methylene-blue test. *See* **stability test**.

metric system. *See* **International Sytem of Units** (SI).

micelle. A unit built up from complex molecules in colloids, which can alter in size without undergoing a chemical change.

micellization-demicellization process. A process of French origin for improving the quality of a biologically-treated sewage, involving passage through a microstrainer, treatment with ozone to demicellize (or neutralize the charge on) the colloidal matter by the oxidizing action of the ozone, with its consequent precipitation and removal by sand filtration.

Michaelis Constant (K_m) The concentration of substrate at which an enzyme reacts with the substrate at a rate equal to one half the maximum rate which occurs when the substrate is present in excess.

microbial film. *See* **biological film**.

microbiology. The study of micro-organisms.

micro-organism. A living organism invisible or barely visible to the naked eye because of its small size; some, however, produce colonies of macroscopic size e.g. sewage fungus *(Sphaerotilus)*.

microscreen. *See* **microstrainer**.

microstrainer. A machine first used for clarifying biologically-treated sewage at Luton in 1950, consisting of a drum covered on the periphery with a stainless-steel fabric of special weave, revolving on an horizontal axis and partially submerged. The liquid to be filtered enters the drum at one end and passes through the fabric, solids being retained on the inner surface. As the drum rotates the solids are continuously washed from the fabric into a collecting trough by pumping effluent through jets fitted on top of the machine. Also termed a 'microscreen'.

milligrammes per litre (mg/l). Used for expressing concentration of impurities in a wastewater or effluent. Term has replaced parts per million (ppm). In SI units the equivalent is gm/m^3 .

milling. A preliminary to scouring cotton pieces. After weaving, the pieces are beaten in a strong solution of soap; this may also contain soda ash, fuller's earth and other materials.

milli-screen. A screen with apertures of 0.25 to 3mm.

mimic diagram. A diagram of a treatment process or works on which are indicated, usually by coloured lights, which units are in service, those on standby, and those which are out of service for maintenance, adjustment or repair.

Minamata disease. A human disease closely associated with the presence of mercury in food, first described as a result of the pathological effects results from the discharge of a mercury-containing industrial wastewater into Minamata Bay, Japan.

minimum acceptable discharge. The minimum discharge, or level corresponding thereto (defined from time to time by the regulatory authority having regard to the needs of all interests downstream), below which the flow in the river or stream at the point of reference should not be diminished by abstractions.

minimum acceptable flow. As defined in the Water Resources Act 1991, section 21(5), this is the minimum flow in a watercourse at a specified point which in the opinion of the Authority is necessary for safeguarding public health and for meeting the requirements of existing lawful users of the water, whether for agriculture, industry, water supply or other purposes, and for the requirements of land drainage, navigation and fisheries, both in relation to that water and to other waters whose flow may be affected by changes in the flow.

mitosis. The process by which a nucleus divides into two; chromosomes appear and divide so that the daughter cells receive identical sets.

mixed-flow pump. A centrifugal pump in which the head is developed partly by centrifugal force and partly by the lift of the vanes on the liquid.

mixed liquor. A mixture of settled sewage and activated sludge undergoing circulation and aeration in the aeration tank or channels of an activated-sludge plant.

mixed liquor suspended solids (MLSS). The weight of dry solids in milligrammes per litre of mixed liquor in the aeration tank or channels of an activated-sludge plant.

mixed-media filter. A filter used for the tertiary treatment of sewage in which there are several media with some intermixing to eliminate stratification and to give an overall graduation in particle size from top to bottom of the filter.

mixed sludge. A mixture of primary sludge and secondary sludge, either raw or digested.

mixing zone. The body of water immediately adjacent to an effluent outfall in which dilution of the discharge is taking place and hence in which the concentration of a pollutant may exceed the maximum concentration set for the main body of the receiving water.

modified aeration. A modification of the activated-sludge process, now obsolete, introduced by L.R. Setter in New York in 1943, in which an intermediate degree of treatment was provided by aerating a mixture of settled sewage and activated sludge for from 1.5 to 2 hours, with the suspended solids content of the mixed liquor ranging from 300 to 600 mg/l.

module. 1. A unit used as a standard of measurement; the size of a certain part of a structure used to determine the proportions of the rest. 2. A device used for controlling the rate of flow of a liquid or for delivering a definite quantity.

Mogden formula. A formula for calculating the charge for treating an industrial wastewater, used for the first time in connection with the treatment of industrial wastewaters at the Mogden works serving the western part of Middlesex. The original formula was as follows:

$$\text{Charge (pence/1000 gal)} = 1 + \frac{M}{75} + \frac{S}{60},$$

where M is the McGowan strength of the settled industrial wastewater (parts per 100 000), S is the suspended solids content of the industrial waste (parts per 100 000), 60 was a factor based on the cost of sludge disposal and 75 was a factor based on the cost of biological treatment of the sewage at Mogden in 1936. Various modified forms of this formula are now in use.

Mohlman Index. *See* **sludge volume index**.

moisture trap. A trap fitted at the lowest point of a main conveying sludge gas from primary digestion tanks, to collect water separating from the gas.

molar solution. A solution containing one mole or gramme molecular weight of the solute in one litre of solution.

molasses slop. When yeast or industrial alcohol is made from molasses, molasses slop is the residue after recovery of the alcohol by distillation.

Mollusca. The phylum of invertebrate animals which includes snails, mussels, oysters, limpets and cockles.

Mono mutrator. A trade name for a combined pump and disintegrator, which rejects solids which cannot be disintegrated, pumps the remainder and disintegrates the solids so that they can be pumped through a small-bore pipeline.

most probable number (MPN). A statistical estimate of the numbers of viable bacteria obtained in a dilution count, such as the presumptive coliform count, in which a series of tubes containing a selective growth medium is inoculated with specified volumes of sample, and incubated. The most probable number is obtained by examining the tubes for a positive growth response (such as production of acid and gas for coliforms) and referring the pattern of such responses to statistical tables.

MPN. *See* **most probable number**.

multiple-hearth dryer-incinerator. A unit first used in the USA in 1934 for drying or incinerating sludge cake, consisting of a vertical firebrick-lined cylinder with a series of four or more hearths, one above the other. Passing up through the centre of the cylinder is a vertical revolving column carrying hollow rotating arms supporting ploughs or rakes. Sludge is fed onto the uppermost hearth and then falls downward from hearth to hearth through ports so arranged that the sludge takes a zigzag path, being swept across the hearths, alternately towards the centre and then towards the periphery. Sludge gas, fuel oil or pulverized coal is injected into the incinerator as an auxiliary fuel at suitable points. Cooling air is admitted to the central column and passes through the hollow arms supporting the ploughs and into the incinerator where it becomes part of the combustion air supply. The gases travel counter-current to the sludge and are vented from the top of the incinerator, passing through dust arrestors to a stack. Drying of the sludge takes place in the top part of the incinerator, followed by combustion in the middle and lower parts, ash being removed from the bottom.

Muncher. A trade name for a proprietary design of screenings disintegrator for sewage or sludge. The machine is a twinshaft, slow-speed, high-torque grinder.

mutagenicity testing. Assessment of the tendency of a substance to give rise to mutations in genetic material e.g. by the Ames Test.

mutation. A change in the characteristics of an organism, arising through a change in gene construction of the nucleus.

mycelium. An interwoven mass of filaments (hyphae) forming the vegetative stage of growth of fungi.

N

Naididae. A family of small oligochaete worms common in freshwaters e.g. *Nais*.

nappe. A sheet of water flowing over a weir.

National Measurement Accreditation Scheme (NAMAS). The UK scheme for accreditation of laboratory facilities. A quality assurance programme run by the Department of Trade and Industry. Similar in nature to BS 5750 and ISO 9000. Assessors regularly and randomly audit each laboratory which must demonstrate adherence to their published procedures, the use of AQC and retention of data and relevant reports for five years.

National Rivers Authority (NRA). A national body to manage estuarial and river waters in England and Wales created by the Water Act 1989.

Nematoda. A phylum of non-segmented round worms, some of which are parasitic, e.g. *Ascaris*. Others are free-living in mud and water; they are small and exhibit a characteristic sinuous movement.

nesslerization. Estimation of the concentration of ammonia in a wastewater or effluent from its reaction with a solution of potassium mercuric iodide in potassium hydroxide solution.

neuston. Aquatic organisms living at the air/water interface, either above it, e.g. water skaters, or hanging below it, e.g. mosquito larvae.

neutron scattering technique. A technique developed by the Water Pollution Research Laboratory in 1962 for measuring the amount of biological film and associated water in a biological filter, and hence the proportion of void space occupied by the film. A source of fast neutrons is attached to a probe containing a counter sensitive to slow neutrons which is inserted in a tube driven into a filter. The neutrons lose energy by repeated collisions with surrounding nuclei, hydrogen nuclei being much more effective in causing loss of energy than heavier elements; also the probability of collision with them is relatively high. The counting rate is roughly proportional to the amount of film in the filter.

niche. That set of ecological conditions under which a species can successfully exploit an energy source in an ecosystem.

night soil. The contents of cesspools, usually removed at night.

nitrate sensitive area. A defined geographical area, designated by statutory order, within which land use is controlled to minimise the leaching of nitrates to ground and surface waters used for potable supply.

nitrification. The oxidation of ammonia to nitrate. Usually carried out by autotrophic bacteria which obtain their energy from the oxidation reaction.

nitrifying filter. A biological filter used for giving further treatment to the effluent from an activated-sludge plant or biological-filter plant to complete the oxidation of ammoniacal nitrogen to nitrate

Nitrobacter. A bacterium which converts nitrite to nitrate.

nitrogen balance. The relation between input and output of nitrogen in an ecological system, e.g. in a lake, river or sewage-treatment works.

nitrogen cycle. The cycle of processes by which nitrogen and its compounds are utilized and transformed in nature.

Nitrosomonas. A bacterium capable of oxidizing ammonia to nitrite.

Nitzschia palea. A common species of diatom of value as an indicator organism of organic pollution.

'no-grazing' period. The stipulated period for the non-grazing of animals following an application of sewage sludge.

nomogram or **nomograph**. A graph which enables the value of a variable to be found when the values of two other variables are known, a common form being three parallel lines graduated in such a way that a straight line joining the two known variables crosses the third line at the corresponding value of the unknown variable.

non-ionic detergent. *See* **synthetic detergent**.

non-return valve. *See* **check valve**.

normal solution. A solution which, per litre, contains the equivalent weight of the particular substance in grammes, the equivalent weight being the weight of the substance in grammes which, in the particular reaction under consideration, combines with or displaces 1 gramme-atom of hydrogen.

NTA. Abbreviation for nitrilotriacetic acid, a substitute for phosphates in synthetic detergents. *See* **chelating agent**, **complexing agent**.

nuclide. A species of atom, characterized by its atomic number, mass number and energy content. *See* **radionuclide**.

nutrient. The food of specific organisms. Nutrients commonly understood to mean plant nutrients such as nitrogen and phosphorus in water.

nymph. The larval stage of an aquatic exopterygote insect which resembles to some extent the adult (imago), e.g. mayflies, and dragon-flies. The developing wings can be seen in the final stages of the larva.

O

Odonata. Dragon-flies, an order of insects having aquatic larval stages.

Oligochaeta. True segmented worms having chaetae (bristles). Many species are aquatic, some being found in biological filters and a few in activated sludge.

oligosaprobic. The final zone of recovery from organic pollution according to the saprobien system.

oligotrophic. Applied to fresh waters, a condition of low nutrient concentration (particularly nitrogen and phosphorus) which restricts primary productivity.

oocyst. The environmentally resistant transmissible form of *Cryptosporidium* excreted in the faeces of an infected host. *See* **Cryptosporidium**.

open-loop process control. A method of controlling a continuous-flow process, involving the initial setting by manual operation and assuming that a steady state will be maintained, with no deviation from the desired result. *See* **process control techniques**.

Opercularia. A genus of colonial peritrichous ciliate protozoan common in activated sludge and used an an indicator of its condition.

Ordnance Datum (OD). Mean sea level at Newlyn, Cornwall; the levelling datum used by the Ordnance Survey.

organelle. A specialised part of the cell approximately analogous to the organ of a higher animal.

organic carbon. Carbon in a form of chemical combination in which it may formally be converted to carbon dioxide by oxidation; carbonates and carbon dioxide are excluded by definition and by the method of analysis. Normally carbon dioxide (present in the sample or formed by acidification of carbonates) is driven off by preliminary treatment, leaving organic carbon for determination. Or the carbon dioxide may be determined by a specific method and subtracted from 'total carbon' determined by analysis to give organic carbon by difference.

organic matter. Material of animal or vegetable origin. Nowadays, however, applied to all compounds of carbon other than those generally regarded as inorganic, namely carbon dioxide, carbonates, and metallic carbides.

organic pollution. The pollution of a receiving water due to the consequences of the breakdown of excessive concentrations of putrescible organic matter.

organic polymer. A synthetic organic dispersible polymer used as an organic flocculating agent in the conditioning of sludge before dewatering, or in water treatment.

orifice meter. Used for measuring flows of clean water and of air. A thin metal plate with a sharp-edged circular orifice is installed in the pipe-line conveying the air or water, at right angles to the direction of flow. The difference in pressure at a point a short distance upstream of the orifice and at the orifice is measured and this can be related to the rate of flow, variations of which are recorded on a chart.

orifice plate. A metal plate with a central orifice of smaller diameter than the pipeline in which it is installed by inserting it between flanges; used for measuring the flow of air or liquid through the pipeline.

Orsat apparatus. A portable apparatus for determining the proportions of carbon dioxide, oxygen, and carbon monoxide in flue, furnace or exhaust gases. The gas passes through solutions which absorb, successively, the CO_2, O_2 and CO, the diminution in volume of the gas after passing through each solution being a measure of the quantity of each constituent gas.

ortho-phosphate. Common form of inorganic phosphorus. Basic unit is PO_4. *See* **polyphosphate**.

Oscillatoria. A filamentous blue-green alga, found in nutrient-enriched waters, the filaments of which exhibit movement which is visible only under a microscope.

Oslo Convention. The agreement, made in February 1972, by twelve west European countries to ban certain types of dumping in the North Sea and Atlantic between Greenland and Europe, as far south as Gibraltar.

osmoregulation. The process in which an organism regulates the salinity of its internal body fluids in relation to the outside medium.

osmosis. The tendency for pure water to diffuse through a semi-permeable membrane to equalize the concentration when the membrane separates two solutions containing the same solute but in different concentrations. cf. **reverse osmosis**.

osmotrophic. Absorbing food in soluble form as in the case of fungi, bacteria and some protozoa.

outfall. The site of discharge of a liquid from a pipe. Applied particularly to the point at which a sewer discharges to a treatment works or receiving water, or the point at which a conduit discharges the effluent from a treatment works into a receiving water.

outfall sewer. The final length of sewer which conveys the whole of the sewage from a sewerage system to a treatment works or a receiving water, or the pipeline which conveys the effluent from a sewage treatment works to a receiving water.

overflow. *See* **storm overflow**.

overflow weir. *See* **storm overflow**.

oxidation. The chemical change which a substance undergoes when it takes up oxygen.

oxidation ditch or channel. A method of treating crude or settled sewage introduced by A. Pasveer in Holland in 1958, in which two parallel channels are joined at the ends to form a closed circuit and are equipped with one or more aeration rotors, used for aerating a mixture of sewage and activated sludge prior to separation and reuse of the activated sludge and discharge of the effluent to a receiving water.

oxidation pond. *See* **stabilization pond**.

oxidation-reduction potential (ORP). The electromotive potential existing between any solution and a standard hydrogen electrode. A positive potential indicates a state of the environment which is predominantly oxidizing or aerobic; a negative potential indicates a state which is predominantly reducing or anaerobic. Also termed 'redox potential'.

oxygen balance. The dissolved-oxygen concentration in a river depends on the interaction of processes which supply and remove oxygen. The natural immediate sources of oxygen present in water are the atmosphere and, during photosynthesis, aquatic plants (including algae); oxygen is removed through the respiration of aquatic plants, by mud deposits, by suspended bacteria utilizing dissolved or suspended organic matter, and as the result of chemical oxidation of substances discharged to or produced in the water body. Oxygen can be lost to the atmosphere if the water is supersaturated with oxygen with respect to air. The interaction of these gains and losses produces an equilibrium which is referred to as the oxygen balance.

oxygen consumed. *See* **permanganate value, chemical oxygen demand**.

oxygen deficiency. *See* **oxygen deficit**.

oxygen deficit. The difference between the dissolved-oxygen concentration of an aqueous solution and the air saturation value.

oxygen sag curve. The graphic representation of the dissolved oxygen-profile along a polluted river or estuary, exhibiting the (marked) drop in oxygen content below the point of entry of pollution, the effect of self-purification, and the increase in the oxygen content downstream due to the rate of reaeration exceeding the rate of utilization as a secondary function of earlier self-purification.

oxygen saturation value. The concentration of dissolved oxygen in equilibrium with air or pure oxygen. Varies with temperature, pressure (total and partial) and salinity.

oxygen transfer coefficient. The mass-transfer coefficient for oxygen. Also termed 'exit coefficient', 'aeration coefficient', 'exchange coefficient'.

oxygenation capacity. The rate of transfer of oxygen in grammes per cubic metre per hour into fully deoxygenated water in an aeration tank at a specified temperature, usually either 10°C or 20°C and specified pressure.

oxygenation efficiency. The oxygenation capacity per unit of power supplied to an aeration system at a given temperature and pressure.

ozonation. The addition of ozone, particularly to a raw water or biologically-treated sewage to decolorize and disinfect it. Also termed 'ozonization' .

P

Pachydrilus. Or *Lumbricillus*; worms of the family Enchytraeidae, commonly found as a grazer in biological filters.

package-deal sewage-treatment plant. A sewage-treatment plant for which a single firm has contracted to design, supply and construct the whole of the plant.

package sewage-treatment plant. A sewage-treatment plant which is fabricated at the factory and is taken to the site as a complete unit ready for use. Also termed 'packaged sewage-treatment plant'.

packed tower filter. A biological filter, first used in the UK about 1960, which exceeds 2.5 metres in height and is packed with synthetic plastics media.

paddle-aeration system. An early method of surface aeration used in the activated-sludge process, introduced by J. Haworth at Sheffield in 1916, in which a mixture of settled sewage and activated sludge flows along a continuous shallow channel up to 0.8 km long, aeration and mixing being induced by the motion of waves created by a series of paddle wheels rotating about a horizontal axis.

paddle aerator. An aerator used in the paddle-aeration system.

paper manufacture. In the manufacture of paper from pulp the following processes are involved: (a) preparation of pulp by mixing in a 'beater' with water to which substances to be incorporated in the finished paper have been added; (b) pulp, diluted with water, flows through a flow-regulating box, sand traps and screens; (c) pulp delivered to paper-making machine; (d) partially-dried sheet of paper passes over heated rolls to evaporate remaining water. Wastewaters include those from the paper machine, called 'backwater' and 'white water', and floor washings.

paramagnetic oxygen analyser. An instrument consisting of a cell into which the gas to be tested passes and in which is pivoted a dumb-bell shaped container of nitrogen which is surrounded by an electromagnetic field. When a paramagnetic gas (such as oxygen) enters the gas space, the container rotates, and since it carries a mirror, its reflection can be followed by the movements of a reflected beam of light on a translucent screen. The container can be restored to its original position by changing the strength of the electromagnetic field by the use of a potentiometer. Since the deflection is proportional to the concentration of paramagnetic gas, the potentiometer can be calibrated as percentage of oxygen.

Paramecium. A genus of free-swimming ciliate protozoa common in activated sludge and a useful indicator organism.

parameter. *See* **determinand**.

parasite. An organism which lives on another organism (the host) from which it obtains its nutrition, often to the detriment of the host.

partially-separate system. A modification of the separate sewerage system in which part of the surface water and the whole of the wastewater are conveyed by the same drains and sewers.

parts per billion (ppb). Parts per thousand million. Former usage in the UK was 'parts per million million' but the US usage is now generally accepted. Where there is a possibility of doubt the unit should be defined.

parts per million (ppm). Used at one time for expressing concentrations of impurities in a wastewater or effluent. Equivalent to milligrammes per litre.

pasteurisation. A method of destroying pathogenic organisms in sludge by heating it to a high temperature for a relatively short period of time (e.g. to 70°C for 30 minutes).

Pasveer ditch. *See* **oxidation ditch or channel**.

pathogen. An organism which is capable of producing disease.

pathogenic bacteria. *See* **pathogen**.

Paxman sludge concentrator. *See* **Roto-Plug sludge concentrator**.

PCB. See **polychlorinated biphenyls**.

peat bed. A biological method of odour treatment. Odorous air is passed into the bottom of a bed made up of layers of peat and heather, and micro-organisms absorb and oxidise odorous compounds to carbon dioxide, water, sulphates and nitrates.

pebble-bed clarifier. *See* **upward-flow clarifier**.

penstock. A device incorporating a vertically sliding gate installed in a channel or at the inlet or outlet of a tank or chamber for the purpose of controlling the magnitude and direction of the flow. It may have either a rising spindle or a non-rising spindle.

percolating filter. *See* **biological filter**.

perforated-pipe distributor. A method of distribution used in the early days of biological filtration in which pipes with orifices at intervals were laid on or supported above the surface and through which settled sewage was applied to a biological filter. *See* **stationary distributor**.

periodicity of dosing. The time lapse between successive applications of sewage to a biological filter.

peripheral weir. The weir extending round the circumference of a circular or square tank, over which the effluent discharges.

periphyton. Strictly, organisms living on the stems and leaves of aquatic plants. Extended to those organisms on other objects standing out of the bottom, e.g. posts, etc.

peristaltic pump. A pump used in laboratories, in some portable samplers and in dosing equipment. In one design a liquid flowing through a flexible tube is split into sections by fingers on a rotating disk pressing the tube against the curved bed. As the disk rotates the slug of liquid in the section between two fingers is carried forward.

Peritricha. An order of ciliate protozoa, many of which are bell-shaped and attached by stalks to a substratum. Several genera are found in activated sludge, e.g. *Vorticella, Opercularia, Carchesium*.

permanent hardness. A characteristic of water, chiefly due to the presence of chlorides and sulphates of calcium and magnesium. When soap is used the water does not lather readily and such hardness is not removed by boiling. Also termed 'non-carbonate hardness'.

permanganate index. A non-specific rapid (10 min) measure of the oxygen taken up from permanganate in an acidified sample. Suitable for potable or lightly polluted water. cf. **permanganate value**.

permanganate value (PV). Oxygen absorbed from acidified N/80 potassium permanganate during four hours at 27°C. The test is empirical and of somewhat restricted value. cf. **permanaganate index**.

permeability. The permeability of a ceramic diffuser as used in the activated-sludge process is the quantity of free air, in cubic metres per minute at 21°C and 25 per cent relative humidity, which will pass to the atmosphere through 0.3 square metre of a diffuser plate 25 millimetres thick under a differential pressure equivalent to 50 millimetres of water below the plate, when tested dry.

persistent organic compounds. Organic compounds which are potentially hazardous, or otherwise undesirable, but which are resistant to degradation by conventional treatment processes.

pesticide. A chemical, natural or synthetic, used to control or eliminate plant or animal life considered detrimental to man's interest, e.g. algicides for the control of algae, herbicides for the control of plants, fungicides for the control of fungi, nematocides for the control of nematodes, molluscicides for the control of snails, insecticides for the control of insects, and piscicides for the control of fish. A larvicide is a pesticide used against the larval stage of an animal.

petrochemicals. Chemicals derived from petroleum or natural gas or from one of its derivatives. Wastewaters may be derived from the conversion of naphtha to ethylene, propylene and other olefins, and high aromatic liquid fractions. Ethylene oxide may be produced by the direct oxidation process or the chloro-hydrin process. Also involves the manufacture of such materials as polystyrene and high-density polyethylene and polypropylene.

pH value. A measure of the acidity or alkalinity of an aqueous solution, expressed as the logarithm, base 10, of the inverse of the hydrogen ion concentration, this being the weight of hydrogen ions in grammes per litre of solution multiplied by the activity coefficient, which is close to unity in most fresh waters and in other waters of relatively low ionic strength. Most aqueous solutions have pH values in the range 0 to 14, with pure water (which is neutral) having a pH value of 7. Values above and below 7 indicate alkalinity and acidity respectively.

phagotrophic. Feeding by engulfing particulate matter. cf. **osmotrophic**.

Phelps' Law. A formula introduced by E.B. Phelps of the USA in 1912, postulating that the rate of biochemical oxidation of a wastewater by bacteria proceeds in conformity with the equation:

$$\log_{10} \frac{L}{L - x} = kt$$

where L is the first stage, or carbonaceous oxygen demand (usually satisfied in about 20 days), x is the oxygen demand (in mg/l) in t days (as determined by the BOD test) and k is a constant. The formula has no theoretical significance and samples conforming to it do so as the result of summation of numerous more complex reactions.

phenolphthalein. Colourless crystals with the formula $C_{20}H_{14}O_4$ which, when dissolved in alcohol, produce a deep purple-red colour in the presence of an alkali. Used as an indicator in volumetric analysis.

phenolphthalein alkalinity. *See* **alkalinity**.

phenols. A group of aromatic organic compounds having the hydroxyl group directly attached to the benzene nucleus. They are highly toxic to living organisms and can adversely affect biological sewage-treatment processes or sludge digestion although, under suitable conditions, they can be broken down by biological treatment.

Phoredox process. A process for the biological removal of nitrogen and phosphorus developed by Barnard in South Africa in 1974. Settled sewage and returned activated sludge pass through an anaerobic zone in which phosphate is released from the cells of the micro-organisms in the sludge into the liquid phase. In the following aeration zone the phosphate is taken up by the sludge, in an amount in excess of the metabolic requirement (luxury uptake). The phosphate-rich sludge is removed from the system.

Phormidium. A blue green alga the filaments of which interwine to form a sheet. Common on the surface of biological filters where it may cause ponding.

photosynthesis. The synthesis of carbohydrates using chlorophyll, by green, blue, yellow and brown pigment-bearing organisms, plants, algae and some phytoflagellates, from atmospheric carbon dioxide and water in the presence of sunlight.

physico-chemical processes. The treatment of sewage by chemical and physical processes which do not make use of biological agencies.

phytoplankton. Free-floating algae. They are mostly very small and occur mainly near the surface, where the aquatic plants receive suitable illumination. Can develop into large numbers termed blooms.

phytotoxic. A substance which is toxic to plants and algae.

picket-fence thickener. A circular tank equipped with a slowly rotating device comprising vertical bars to assist separation of water and consolidation of sludge in the tank. *See* **thickening**.

pickling. Removal of scale from iron and steel, or from copper and copper alloys before annealing. Scale removed by immersing the metal in a bath of warm pickling solution, usually consisting of sulphuric or hydrochloric acid in the case of iron and steel, sulphuric acid for copper and brass, and a mixture of sulphuric and nitric acids for copper alloys. With iron and steel an inhibiting agent may be added to the solution. After pickling, the metal is washed with water. Wastewaters include spent pickle liquor and washwaters.

pig. A device which can be pulled through a pipe, or forced through by hydraulic pressure, to scrape the inside of the pipe and displace debris and encrustation.

piggery wastes. The volume and character of piggery wastewaters depends on the system of housing and management. With traditional methods of housing the wastes consist of semi-solid manure, urine and floor washings, wash-down water from yards, and rainwater.

Pista grit trap. A circular grit-separating tank introduced by S.A. Pista in Switzerland in 1962. Sewage enters the tank tangentially and the vortex created, assisted by a rotating paddle, keeps the organic matter in suspension so that it passes out with the sewage whilst the grit settles into a sump from which it is removed by an air-lift pump. *See* **Jeta grit trap**.

piston pump. *See* **reciprocating pump**.

pitot tube. A device for measuring the pressure of a fluid flow and therefore its velocity, consisting essentially of a tube with two openings, one turned upstream and the other downstream, the difference in pressure created in the tube between the two openings being measured by a manometer.

Planarians. Free-living flat worms of the order Turbellaria. Common in fresh water and used as an indicator of river quality.

plankton (≡drifting). Organisms which live suspended in the water, although some are capable of independent movement. They are largely carried by the currents.

plastics filter medium. A fabricated plastics packing specially designed for use as a medium in a biological filter. Some packings are light in weight, have a high surface area per unit volume, and a large proportion of voids. Most of the media produced commercially have comprised an ordered packing of thin semi-rigid, corrugated sheets of various degrees of complexity made from polystyrene or polyvinyl chloride. Random-fill media are also available.

plastid. An organelle in a plant or algal cell that contains the photosynthetic pigment.

plate counts. Total viable plate counts are counts of culturable aerobic organisms including bacteria, yeasts and moulds. They are used to assess the general microbial quality of water. Commonly divided into two groups: those culturing most readily at 22°C and those at 37°C respectively.

plate diffuser. *See* **porous air-diffuser**.

Plecoptera. Commonly known as stone-flies, the aquatic larvae of which live in upland streams and are an indicator of well-aerated water.

plug-flow system. An arrangement whereby the sewage to be treated in an activated-sludge plant and the returned sludge are mixed and then introduced into one end of a long aeration tank or channel or a tank containing several baffle walls, the treated mixed liquor being withdrawn at the other end. With this arrangement there is a substrate concentration gradient along the length of the tank or channel. Also termed 'piston flow'. cf. **complete-mixing system**.

plug valve. A valve in which the movable control element is a cylindrical or conical plug with a waterway through it, in contrast to a flat disc. With a 'lubricated plug valve' a lubricant is injected under pressure between the plug and its seating to reduce friction.

plunger pump. *See* **reciprocating pump**.

pneumatic ejector. A device introduced by I. Shone about 1878 for raising sewage, sludge or other liquid by alternately admitting it through a non-return valve into an airtight vessel and then discharging it through another non-return valve by admitting compressed air to the vessel above the sewage or sludge.

polishing process. *See* **tertiary treatment**.

polluting load. The quantity of polluting matter entering a treatment plant or in the effluent discharged into a receiving water during a given period.

pollution. The impairment of the suitability of water for some considered purpose.

polychlorinated biphenyls (PCB). These compounds were produced from biphenyl and contain different percentages of chlorine, each product being a mixture containing many different isomers. The commercial products are chemically inert, fire-resistant, fat-soluble and of low solubility in water. The isomers containing low numbers of chlorine atoms per molecule may be slowly degraded, but those containing higher numbers tend to be stored in fatty tissues of organisms. PCBs were used in heat-transfer and hydraulic systems, in fire-resistant adhesive and resin formulations, in carbonless reproducing papers, and as dielectric liquids in electrical transformers and capacitors. They have been shown to be very persistent in the environment, passing along food chains to higher animals. Production and use are now prohibited in most countries.

polyelectrolytes. A general term used for a wide range of natural and synthetic, water-soluble, macromolecular compounds having the ability to flocculate dispersed systems. They are usually polymers with a large number of ionizable groups, but the term is also used for flocculants such as polyethylene oxides of high molecular weight, which are not strictly polyelectrolytes. They are used in water and wastewater treatment either alone or in conjunction with inorganic coagulants, for promoting the sedimentation and filtration of suspended solids, and for conditioning sludges before dewatering.

polyglycol. Chemically a self-condensation product of ethylene oxide. Commercial products of a relatively high molecular weight are essentially water-soluble oils or waxes forming minor constituents (possibly up to 4 per cent) of commercially-available brands of non-ionic surface-active agents. Used in industry e.g. as thread lubricants. Polyglycols of low molecular weight are formed as breakdown products of non-ionic detergents.

polymer. A substance consisting of macromolecules, each composed of an indefinite number of simpler molecules. Polymers may be natural, e.g. cellulose, or manufactured, e.g. polythene.

polyphosphate. Linked ortho-phosphate units, e.g. sodium triphosphate, $Na_5P_3O_{10}$, a major ingredient of heavy-duty washing powders. Partially hydrolysed to ortho-phosphate during passage to or through the sewage-treatment works.

polysaprobic. The most polluted zone according to the saprobien system of classification. Characterized by serious deoxygenation, a marked restriction in the numbers of invertebrates, and high bacterial numbers.

ponding. Choking of the interstices of the medium in a biological filter to the extent that pools of applied liquid appear on the surface.

population equivalent. The volume and strength of an industrial wastewater expressed in terms of an equivalent population, based upon a figure of 0.060 kilogramme BOD *per capita* per day; the population equivalent of an industrial wastewater is therefore calculated using the relationship.

$$\text{Population equivalent} = \frac{\text{5-day BOD (mg/l)} \times \text{flow (m}^3\text{/d)}}{0.060 \times 10^3}$$

Porifera. Sponges; a phylum of primitive invertebrate animals having a colonial sedentary mode of life forming sponge-like growth. Mostly marine but with a few freshwater species.

porosity. The porosity of a diffuser used in the activated-sludge process is defined as the percentage ratio of pore space by volume to the bulk volume of the diffuser material.

porous air-diffuser. A device used in the activated-sludge process for introducing air into the mixed liquor. It may take the form of a porous plate, tube or dome, constructed of silicon dioxide or aluminium oxide grains held in a porous mass with a ceramic binder. Air under pressure is introduced under the plate or within the tube or dome and in passing through is broken up into bubbles ranging in size from 1.25 to 3.0 mm diameter.

porous pot apparatus. A laboratory scale activated-sludge unit originally devised by the Water Pollution Research Laboratory. The feed and mixed liquor are aerated in a porous pot through which the treated effluent percolates, eliminating the need for a settlement tank.

Porteous process. *See* **heat treatment**.

pot ale. In the manufacture of whisky, pot ale is the residue from the first distillation of the fermented liquor. It is also known as 'burnt ale' or 'spent wash'.

Potamogeton. Pondweed, which is an aquatic macrophyte with many species growing in ponds and rivers.

potamology. The branch of hydrology pertaining to receiving waters.

potcher. A special tank in which esparto pulp is washed with water. It is oval and has a central partition round which the pulp is circulated, fresh water being added continuously and used water withdrawn.

potentially toxic elements (PTE). Certain heavy metals and other elements in sludge which are toxic to plants and animals.

poultry wastes. The volume and character of wastewaters from intensive poultry units depend on the system used for handling and storing the wastes. They usually consist of wash-down water contaminated with faecal matter. If the poultry are processed the waste will contain blood, feathers and offal.

power-driven reciprocating-arm distributor. *See* **reciprocating-arm distributor**.

power-driven rotating-arm distributor. *See* **rotating-arm distributor**.

power-driven squeegee. A type of scraper used in horizontal-flow sedimentation tanks which were designed for manual cleaning but have since been modified. A scraper blade is attached to a light tractor or bulldozer which is lowered into the tank by a crane or runs into the tank down a specially constructed ramp.

preaeration. The aeration of sewage for a short period prior to sedimentation, or of settled sewage prior to biological treatment.

precision. A measure of how closely a set of results are grouped together. Often expressed as confidence limits. Results can be precise and inaccurate. *See* **accuracy**.

preliminary treatment. The removal or disintegration of gross solids in sewage and the removal of grit. Also sometimes the removal of oil and grease from sewage, prior to sedimentation.

prescribed concentration value (PCV). Used in the Water Act 1989 to define the upper or maximum concentration or level permitted of a measurable parameter in water used for potable supply.

prescriptive right. The right conferred on a manufacturer, under the Public Health (Drainage of Trade Premises) Act 1937, who discharged industrial wastewater into the public sewer during the twelve months ended 3 March 1937 to continue discharging the waste into the sewer provided that the daily volume, rate of flow and character of the waste remain the same. *See* **existing discharge**.

press cake. *See* **sludge cake**.

pressure filter. A device for dewatering sludge consisting of a series of ridged plates (usually rectangular), manufactured from cast iron, plastics or rubber bonded onto steel, between which are cloths of jute, cotton, nylon or other synthetic fibre. When closed the plates are pressed together but they are so shaped that there are spaces between the cloths into which the sludge is forced, allowing liquor to pass through the cloths and drain away leaving sludge cake in the press. When the press is opened and the plates parted the cake falls onto a conveyer or direct into a vehicle. Also termed a 'sludge press' or 'filter press'.

pressure filtration. A process used for dewatering sludge in which the sludge, after conditioning, is forced into a pressure filter, in which separation of liquor from solids takes place.

pressure filtration time (PFT) **meter**. An apparatus developed at the Water Research Centre but now manufactured commercially. A bench-top apparatus, measurement of PFT usually takes only a few minutes and the result can be used as a measure of filtrability and also to predict both the pressing time in filter presses and ultimate cake dry solids content.

pressure-reducing valve. A valve which automatically reduces the pressure of a liquid or gas passing through and maintains the reduced pressure on the downstream side irrespective of changes in flow or of the pressure on the upstream side.

pressure relief valve. A safety valve designed to relieve pressure, e.g. when the pressure under the floating cover of a primary sludge digestion tank exceeds the limit at which the valve is set.

pressure-swing adsorption (PSA). A process in which air under pressure is passed through a zeolite molecular sieve where nitrogen is preferentially adsorbed, producing a product gas containing more than 90% oxygen. The bed is regenerated by the removal of the absorbed nitrogen under vacuum or reduced pressure.

pressure transducer. A form of diaphragm located at the bottom of a channel to compare the pressure of the liquid above on one side, with the air pressure on the other. The differential pressure is detected by resistors and converted to voltage from which the depth can be derived.

presumptive coliform count. A dilution tube method for the enumeration of coliform bacteria present in a sample of water or wastewater by their biochemical activity, shown by the production of gas from lactose in the presence of bile salts at 37°C.

pretreatment. The treatment which an industrial wastewater receives at the factory before discharge into the public sewer. Pretreatment of a sludge refers to conditioning before dewatering.

primary clarifier. *See* **sedimentation tank**.

primary digestion tank. *See* **digestion tank**.

primary productivity. In an ecological system, the rate at which energy is stored as a result of the photosynthetic or chemosynthetic activity of the organisms producing it.

primary sedimentation tank. *See* **sedimentation tank**.

primary sludge. Sludge formed from sewage solids removed by settlement in a primary sedimentation tank.

primary treatment. The first major stage of treatment following preliminary treatment in a sewage works, usually involving removal of settleable solids.

cf. **preliminary treatment**.

Primox. A trade name for an injection of oxygen into the pumped sewage entering a rising main in order to prevent septicity occurring and to achieve partial treatment of the sewage during its retention in the main.

private sewer. A sewer which is not a public sewer as defined in section 20 of the Public Health Act 1936.

process control techniques. Techniques for the control of continuous-flow processes, involving (a) the initial setting; (b) assessment or measurement of result; (c) comparison with desired result; (d) estimation or measurement of any deviation; (e) correction if deviation exists. There are six methods of conventional control: (1) open-loop control; (2) manual closed-loop control; (3) automatic closed-loop control; (4) supervisory control; (5) feedforward control and (6) feedback loop. *See* **automatic closed-loop process control, feedforward process control, manual closed-loop process control, open-loop process control, supervisory process control**.

productivity. Ecologically, the production of mass of a population; primary productivity being indicated by the rate of photosynthesis of algae or plants in a community; secondary productivity being the growth of a consumer population.

proteins. Complex nitrogenous substances, usually colloidal, composed mainly of amino acids. Essential constituents of all living cells, being responsible for growth and for making good the wastage of tissue.

Protozoa. A phylum of unicellular micro-organisms. Contains a heterogeneous collection of organisms of considerable diversity of form and nutrition, and comprises four classes. The ones of aquatic significance are characterised by their organelles of locomotion and feeding. These are: (a) flagellates, which have whip-like flagella, e.g. *Euglena*; (b) rhizopoda, with protoplasmic extensions called pseudopodia, e.g. *Amoeba*; (c) ciliata, with hairlike processes termed cilia. e.g. *Paramecium*; (d) sporoza, which are parasitic spore-formers e.g. *Plasmodium* (the malaria parasite).

pseudo-colloidal matter. Very finely divided suspended solids, bordering on colloidal matter, in sewage.

Psychoda. A genus of small moth-like flies the larvae of which are 'grazers' in biological filters.

psychrophilic. Thriving at temperatures below 20°C.

public sewer. A sewer vested in a water company by virtue of the provisions of section 20 of the Public Health Act 1936 as amended by the Water Act 1973 and 1989.

pulp water. Water draining from sugar beet 'cossettes' after extraction of the sugar.

pulverized fuel ash (PFA). Ash from the pulverized fuel used in a power station, sometimes employed as a filter aid in the mechanical dewatering of sludge.

pump. *See* **air-lift pump, axial-flow pump, centrifugal pump, diaphragm pump, disintegrator pump, gas-lift pump, mixed-flow pump, peristaltic pump, reciprocating pump, screw pump, stereophagus pump, submersible pump, Willet pump**.

pump well. A dry well in which pumps are installed when located below ground level.

pupa. The non-feeding stage in the life cycle of an insect which follows the termination of the larval stage. Usually quiescent and develops into the adult or imago stage.

purifier. A bed of moist ferric oxide through which coal gas is passed to remove hydrogen sulphide.

putrefaction. The uncontrolled anaerobic decomposition of the organic matter in sewage when acid-producing bacteria are allowed to predominate.

putrescibility. The relative tendency for wastewater, effluent or sludge to undergo anaerobic decomposition.

pyrometer. An instrument for measuring high temperatures, as in a dual-fuel engine or furnace, a common type of which uses the principle of the thermocouple. *See* **thermocouple**.

Q

Q_{10} (Arrhenius equation). The factor by which the growth or activity of an organism, a physiological process, or an enzymic reaction, increases per 10°C rise in temperature (within physiological limits).

R

rabble arm. The hollow arm attached to the rotating centre shaft in a multiple-hearth incinerator, which supports ploughs or rakes for 'rabbling' the sludge around the refractory hearth.

radial-flow tank. A circular tank with the inlet at the centre, the outlet consisting of a peripheral weir, and the floor being either flat or sloping to a central sump or hopper according to the means employed for withdrawing sludge from the tank.

radioactive tracer. A radioisotope, such as bromine-82 (normally used as potassium bromide), used for (a) measuring the flow of sewage or sludge in sewers or pipelines; (b) determining the pattern of flow in sedimentation tanks, biological filters or an activated-sludge plant; (c) making flow, retention period and dispersion measurements in rivers; (d) studying the dispersion of sewage or sludge in the sea; (e) determining the fate of nutrients or pollutants in biological systems; or (f) studying the pattern of reaction in chemical or biological reactions.

radioactive waste. A waste resulting from the production or subsequent use of radionuclides. Radioactive wastes may be classified as (a) of high activity; (b) of medium activity; or (c) of low activity. High activity wastes are stored indefinitely in specially constructed facilities; medium activity wastes are treated with chemicals and the sludge produced is stored with high activity wastes, the liquid being discharged into the sea or a suitable large river; low activity wastes are disposed of in the same way. Low activity wastes may also be discharged, under strict control, into the public sewer.

radioisotopes. Certain isotopes of all elements are unstable, emitting α, β or γ radiation (or a combination of α, β and γ). Some radioisotopes may be used as tracers. *See* **radioactive tracer**.

radionuclide. There are more than 1300 species of atoms (nuclides), characterised by the number of protons (Z), number of neutrons (N) and energy within the nucleus. Those which decay to form other nuclides — mostly by the emission of an electron or positron — are termed radionuclides. To be classed as a radionuclide the species must be capable of existing for a measurable time. Isomeric states are separate radionuclides whereas promptly decaying nuclear intermediates in nuclear reactions are not. Isotopes are nuclides of the same Z. The three isotopes of hydrogen are hydrogen or protium (Z=1, N=0), deuterium (Z=1, N=1), and tritium (Z=1, N=2). Only tritium is a radionuclide or radioisotope of hydrogen. Isotones are nuclides of the same N and isobars are nuclides of the same N+Z.

rag pulp manufacture. Conversion of rag into pulp for use in the manufacture of high-quality paper, involving the following processes: (a) sorting and treatment to remove dust; (b) digestion under pressure with an alkali; (c) washing; (d) further washing with cold water in a washing engine. Wastewaters include spent liquor and washwaters.

rain-gun. A device for spraying sewage or water over an area of land. Also termed a 'spray-gun'. *See* **manure gun**.

raking mechanism. A power-driven mechanism, controlled either manually or automatically, used for removing gross solids from a sewage screen.

rapid gravity sand filter. A sand filter used for removing suspended solids from biologically-treated sewage by passage downward through a layer of sand supported by a porous medium, and thus into underdrains. The filter is cleaned by periodically reversing the flow of effluent upwards through the medium, sometimes supplemented by air agitation during washing to remove suspended solids lodged in the sand.

rate of hindered settling (RHS). The rate of hindered settling is the rate of fall of the interface between a suspension and its supernatant liquor under the effects of gravity. This is the settling rate observed at the beginning of a settling test (where the sample is well flocculated and has a high enough concentration of suspended solids to form an interface), and the rate remains constant at its maximum value for a time before decreasing in the compaction and compression zones. Hence this settling rate is variously known as (a) maximum settling rate; (b) linear settling rate; (c) initial settling rate, or (d) initial interface velocity. Typically, for a mixed liquor with 3000 mg/l suspended solids, settling rates of 0.5 and 2 m/h would indicate poor and good settling characteristics respectively. If the settling rate is lower than the overflow rate of the sedimentation tank, the settling characteristics are not satisfactory.

raw sludge. Primary sludge or secondary sludge or a mixture of the two, prior to modification of its nature by anaerobic digestion, thermal or other treatment.

Raymond system. A sludge drying process used in the UK between 1951 and 1970 in which the cake from vacuum filters was mixed with sludge which had already been dried, the mixture then passing through a cage mill through which hot gases from a furnace were circulating so that the sludge was broken up into fine particles and dried. It was then separated from the gases in a cyclone separator. Usually known as the C-E Raymond Flash Drying Process.

reaeration. The aeration of a liquid which had previously been deoxygenated. In sewage treatment, the aeration of activated sludge during passage from the secondary settlement tanks to the aeration tanks or channels to maintain aerobic conditions.

reagent. Pure chemical added to, or used in, the analysis for a determinand or parameter.

receiving water. A body of water, flowing or otherwise, such as a stream, river, lake, estuary or the sea.

reciprocating-arm distributor. A machine used for distributing settled sewage over the surface of a rectangular biological filter, consisting of arms travelling to and fro, supported from a central channel or by side walls and driven by waterwheels or by an electric motor through a chain drive of ropes. The sewage is usually siphoned to the distributor arms from a channel. cf. **rotating-waterwheel distributor**.

reciprocating-arm grit washer. A mechanism used for separating organic matter from grit deposited in a detritor, the mechanism being either integral with the detritor or free-standing. It consists of an inclined ramp with the grit being pushed up it by a reciprocating arm with rakes against a counter flow of washwater, the washwater containing the organic matter being discharged into the detritor and the grit leaving through a chute at the top of the ramp. Also termed a 'classifier'. *See* **classifier**.

reciprocating pump. A type of displacement pump consisting essentially of a closed cylinder containing a piston or plunger, as the displacing mechanism, drawing liquid into the cylinder through an inlet valve and forcing it out through an outlet valve. When the piston acts on the liquid in one end of the cylinder the pump is termed single-action and when it acts in both ends it is termed double-action. With a piston pump the piston fits tightly in the cylinder; with a plunger pump, the plunger does not come in contact with the cylinder walls but enters and withdraws through packing glands.

reciprocating-waterwheel distributor. A machine used for distributing settled sewage over the surface of a rectangular biological filter, consisting of one or two waterwheels travelling to and fro, supported by a central feed channel and side walls. When two waterwheels were used, these were connected by ropes and travelled in opposite directions. Waterwheels used both as a means of propulsion and for distributing sewage. Superseded by waterwheel-driven reciprocating distributors. cf. **reciprocating-arm distributors**.

recirculation. As applied to sewage treatment, the return of a proportion of the settled effluent from a biological filter to mix with settled sewage being applied to the filter. Sometimes unsettled effluent is returned to mix with sewage entering the primary sedimentation tanks. Effluent recirculation may also be applied to two-stage filtration, with settled effluent from the secondary filter being recirculated to mix with settled sewage being applied to the primary filter during the night when the sewage flow is low.

reclamation. The treatment of used water to enable it to be reused, either directly or after discharge to receiving water.

recorder. A device that (1) produces a graph showing variations in, for example pressure, depth, volume, velocity of flow, usually over a fixed period, or (2) retains such data in the memory of an electronic system such as a computer.

rectangular distributor. *See* **reciprocating-arm distributor, reciprocating-waterwheel distributor**.

rectangular sedimentation tank. *See* **horizontal-flow tank**.

rectangular weir. A thin-plate measuring weir of rectangular shape, at right angles to the direction of flow. Such a weir is 'full width' when the sides are flush with the sides of the channel, or 'contracted' when the weir does not extend across the full width; it is then said to have 'side contractions'.

recycling. The use more than once of water for the same process, or successive uses of the same water for different processes by one consumer. The utilization of sewage sludge in agriculture is also an example of recycling.

Red List. A list of the most dangerous substances to the water environment. The basis of legislation for the elimination or reduction of pollution of inland and coastal waters is the Dangerous Substances Directive (76/464/EEC). This and other Directives and Conventions list substances considered to be hazardous, and which must be eliminated or controlled. The Red List is the UK version of the Black List and List 1 used in the Directives, and contains the most dangerous substances based on several properties including persistence in the environment, toxicity and bio-accumulation.

redox potential. *See* **oxidation-reduction potential**.

reducing agent. A substance which removes oxygen from, or adds hydrogen to, another substance. During a chemical reaction it loses electrons and becomes oxidized to a higher valency condition, e.g.
$$Sn^{2+} \rightleftharpoons Sn^{4+} + 2e.$$

reed bed process. An artificially constructed wetland of common reeds in which the wastewater can percolate through the pathways created by the stems, leaves, roots and rhizomes of the reeds. It provides a means of treating screened degritted sewage or polishing a partially treated effluent without the need for power.

reflux valve. *See* **check valve**.

regression analysis. A procedure for determining mathematically the relationships, if any, between observed variables and those which can be measured quantitatively.

reinforcement. The provision of an additional sewer which in conjunction with an existing sewer increases overall flow capacity .

relative humidity. The ratio between the actual amount of moisture in the air and that which would be needed to saturate it at the particular temperature, expressed as a percentage.

relief sewer. A second sewer installed to carry flows in excess of the capacity of the existing sewer.

reoxygenation. The replenishment of oxygen in a receiving water (a) from dilution water entering it; (b) by biological reoxygenation due to the photosynthetic activity of plants; and (c) by natural and artificial reaeration. Also termed 'reaeration'.

residual chlorine. Chlorine remaining in solution after a specified period of contact with the liquor being chlorinated, in a form available to act as an oxidant. Also termed 'free residual chlorine', i.e. Cl_2, HOCl, OCl', and 'combined residual chlorine', e.g. chloramines.

respiration. The oxidation of an organic substrate within a cell to release energy; this is an aerobic process and may be determined by measuring the gaseous interchange between an organism and its surrounding medium.

respiration rate. The rate of uptake of dissolved oxygen by unit weight of activated sludge, expressed in milligrammes of oxygen per gramme of dry activated sludge per hour.

respiratory quotient. The ratio of the volume of carbon dioxide produced by an organism to the volume of oxygen used in respiration during the same period.

respirometer. An apparatus for measuring the amount and rate of oxygen uptake by a sample of raw or treated wastewater during incubation. As the dissolved oxygen in the liquor is used up it is replaced by oxygen absorbed from the confined atmosphere above the respiring sample; this, in turn, is replaced by fresh oxygen from an oxygen reservoir. In an automatic respirometer removal of the carbon dioxide formed is practically instantaneous and as the oxygen is added in very small doses, the composition of the atmosphere in the respiration flask remains the same as that of the original air. Also used for measuring the oxygen consumed by natural mud deposits and aquatic animals.

resuscitation apparatus. Apparatus used for resuscitating a person who has been asphyxiated, one type of which automatically applies rhythmic pulses of positive and negative pressure through a face mask, the power and oxygen supply coming from the pressure of oxygen in a cylinder.

retention period. The period during which wastewater is theoretically retained in a particular unit or system, based on the maximum flow, average flow or dryweather flow, as specified e.g. for a tank:

$$\text{Retention period (h)} = \frac{\text{total capacity of tank (m}^3)}{\text{rate of flow (m}^3/\text{d})} \times 24$$

Also termed 'nominal period'. *See* **flow-through period**.

retort-house liquor. Ammoniacal liquor condensing in the hydraulic and foul mains of a coal-gas producing plant.

retting. Process of separating the fibres of flax to enable them to be used, after treatment, in the manufacture of linen, canvas and thread.

retting liquor. A dark brown liquor with a strong smell produced by the retting of flax.

returned activated sludge. That portion of the activated sludge separated from the mixed liquor in secondary settlement tanks which is returned to the aeration tanks.

reverse osmosis. A process for removing dissolved substances, including inorganic salts, from biologically-treated sewage by exerting sufficient pressure to reverse the normal osmotic flow of water through a membrane from a more dilute to a more concentrated solution. cf. **osmosis**.

Reynolds' Number. A dimensionless number proposed by Osborne Reynolds in 1883 for characterizing the type of flow in a pipe or conduit flowing full where the resistance to motion depends on the viscosity of the liquid and the influence of inertia. It is the product of the mean velocity of flow and the diameter or depth of flow in the pipe or conduit divided by the kinematic viscosity of the liquid.

Rhizopoda. A class of Protozoa moving and feeding by protoplasmic extrusions, known as pseudopodia, e.g. *Amoeba*.

rhodamine-B. A reddish soluble dye with carcinogenic properties used in the past for measuring flow, retention periods, and dispersion. However, it tends to absorb on solid particles and surfaces (tank walls, suspended solids) where it is not readily detected, and for accurate work the closely related, but more expensive, rhodamine-WT is preferred.

ridge-and-furrow aeration. A method of aeration formerly used in the activated-sludge process in which diffusers of the plate variety were located at the bottom of furrows running transversely at first and later longitudinally along the length of the aeration tank with ridges in between so that there were no surfaces on which sludge could settle.

ridge-and-furrow irrigation. A method of applying sewage to crops in which the crop is grown on ridges and the sewage flows in shallow furrows between the ridges.

Ringrose lamp. A proprietary make of gas detector lamp in which gas enters a sealed porous pot by diffusion. The gas is brought into contact with an incandescent palladium filament on which any methane present is burned to form carbon dioxide and water. When the resultant water vapour condenses and the carbon dioxide is absorbed by a small container of soda lime, there is a reduction in pressure. The porous pot communicates with a thin copper capsule, and the pressure reduction causes this to contract and close two electrical contacts which actuate a red warning lamp. The detector is powered by a lead battery.

ring-type scraper. A type of scraper formerly used in radial-flow tanks with a 30 degree floor slope to separate activated sludge, in which trailing scraper blades were attached to booms suspended from a ring-shaped rack driven by an electric motor and pinion.

rising main. A pipeline through which a liquid is pumped to a higher level.

rising sludge. A phenomenon occurring in primary sedimentation tanks or secondary settlement tanks when sludge rises to the surface.

river authority. An authority established under the Water Resources Act 1963 to be responsible for the management of the water resources of a river basin, or group of river basins, as a whole, including both surface and ground water. Superseded by water authorities in 1974 and replaced by the NRA in 1989.

river board. An authority established under the River Boards Act 1948, to be responsible for land drainage, fisheries and pollution prevention within its area. Superseded by river authorities in 1963, by water authorities in 1974 and replaced by the NRA in 1989.

river purification board. An authority established under the Rivers (prevention of Pollution) (Scotland) Act 1951, to be responsible from 1954 onwards for the prevention of pollution of streams and rivers in its area. After 16 May 1975 new river purification boards were set up under the Local Government (Scotland) Act 1973.

rolling-tube-apparatus. An apparatus which slowly rotates one or more inclined tubes which, when fed with settled sewage and/or other wastewater, simulates purification in a biological filter.

root-zone process. *See* **reed-bed process**.

rope-band screen. An inclined screen with the lower end submerged in the sewage, consisting of endless wire ropes passing over rollers and moving at such a speed that gross solids retained on the screen formed by the ropes are carried out of the sewage and removed by revolving brushes when at the highest point of travel.

rope-hauled scraper blade. A type of scraper used in horizontal-flow sedimentation tanks which were designed for manual cleaning but have since been modified . A blade spanning the full width of the tank is supported by a frame mounted on two bogies running on rails fixed to the tank floor and hauled by nylon ropes connected to an electrically-driven winch at one end of the tank. The blade may be lowered for forward movement and lifted for reverse.

Rosenblad heat exchanger. A proprietary make of heat exchanger of Swedish origin. It is circular in shape and consists of spiral plates forming spiral passages through which hot water circulates countercurrent to water which is to convey the heat through other heat exchangers to the contents of primary digestion tanks.

Rotameter. A trade name for a float-type variable-area flow meter consisting of a float moving within a vertical graduated tube of uniform taper. As the rate of flow in the tube alters the float rises or falls, changing the area of the annular space to maintain a constant differential pressure across the float. The flow causes the float to rotate (hence the name), so preventing sticking.

rotary distributor. *See* **rotating-arm distributor**, **rotating-waterwheel distributor**.

rotary-kiln dryer. A machine used for drying sludge cake in which the cake after pulverization, is fed into the upper end of a slowly revolving inclined cylinder where it meets a current of hot gas from a furnace. Alternatively, the dryer may consist of two concentric cylinders, the sludge travelling through the annular space and the hot gas through the inner cylinder and then through the annular space, its flow being countercurrent to that of the sludge. The dried sludge is discharged from the lower end of the cylinder and the hot gas passes through a cyclone separator before being discharged to atmosphere.

rotating-arm distributor. A machine used for distributing settled sewage over the surface of a (usually) circular biological filter, consisting of an arm or arms with orifices rotating about a central column and driven by reaction jets, waterwheels or an electric motor. cf. **rotating-waterwheel distributor**.

rotating biological contactor (RBC). A unit consisting of a series of closely-spaced, parallel solid or mesh disks mounted on a shaft which is supported just above the surface of the wastewater to be treated. The lower parts of the disks therefore extend into the waste. When the disks are slowly rotated, the biological film or slime which develops on the wetted surfaces is alternately submerged to absorb nutrients and raised out of the liquid to oxidize the absorbed fraction. Variants of the system use mesh drums containing packings in place of the solid or mesh disks.

rotating half-bridge scraper. A type of scraper used in radial-flow sedimentation tanks and secondary settlement tanks, consisting of a bridge extending from the peripheral wall to the centre of the tank, about which it rotates. The bridge is supported and pivoted at the centre, and at the outer end it is supported by a carriage which travels round the peripheral wall.

rotating-waterwheel distributor. A machine sometimes used for distributing settled sewage over the surface of a small circular biological filter, consisting of a waterwheel rotating about a central vertical feed pipe and supported at the outer end by a runner, the waterwheel being used both as a means of propulsion and for distributing the sewage. Formerly used on larger filters but superseded by waterwheel-driven machines. cf. **rotating-arm ditributor**.

rotavirus. Belonging to the reovirus group and named after their wheel-like appearance under electron microscopy. Numerous strains exist of which three groups (one with six serotypes) have been isolated from humans. Rotaviruses are often spread via contaminated water and are a major cause of the child diarrhoeal syndrome which kills several million children each year, mainly in developing countries.

Rotifera. Or wheel animals; a phylum of multi-cellular microscopic organisms characterised by the possession of ciliated disks. Commonly found in water and in activated sludge.

Roto-Plug sludge concentrator. A machine for dewatering sludge, in which the sludge is fed into a series of revolving drums rotating at about 2.8 revolutions per minute to which are fitted nylon filter cloths. Liquor drains through the cloth, leaving the solids inside the drum the rotation of which causes them to form a cylindrical plug which becomes partly dewatered by its own weight and by the rolling action. As it lengthens, cutters cut off the ends of the rolling mass and these then pass through a compression filter to produce a sludge containing from 20 to 30 per cent solids.

roughing filter. An artificial media filter used in the early days of sewage treatment for straining settled sewage before discharge into a receiving water or application to land. The term was later applied to a biological filter containing a relatively coarse synthetic medium and operated at a high rate to oxidize the readily degradable organic matter in settled sewage before further treatment by conventional biological filtration.

roughness coefficient. *See* **coefficient of roughness**.

Royal Commission. Usually refers to the Royal Commission on Sewage Disposal, which sat from 1898 until 1915 and issued nine reports. However, a

Royal Commission on Environmental Pollution was set up in 1970.

Royal Commission standard. The standard for sewage effluent proposed by the Royal Commission on Sewage Disposal (1898–1915), according to which the effluent should not contain more than 30 mg/l suspended solids and have a BOD not exceeding 20 mg/l, on the assumption that it would be diluted with at least eight volumes of water with a BOD not exceeding 2 mg/l. Often referred to as the '30:20 standard'.

S

sack-screens. *See* **Copa-Sac**.

Salmonella. A group of entero-pathogenic bacteria responsible for typhoid fevers and food poisoning. Common in polluted waters.

samplers. Devices for collecting (a) samples of liquid for analysis; (b) samples of representative organisms from aquatic systems; or (c) samples of bottom deposits. The sampler may be designed for collecting a single sample, single samples at specified intervals, flow-proportional samples, a composite sample, or for continuous sampling, and the samples may be collected manually or the sampler may be operated automatically. *See* **automatic sampler**.

sampling programme. A programme of sampling over a period, e.g. (a) to monitor the load on a sewage-treatment works or receiving water due to an industrial wastewater; (b) to provide fully representative information on the performance of a treatment process or works; or (c) to determine trends in water quality in relation to changes in operational or environmental variables.

sand filter. As used for removing suspended solids from biologically-treated sewage, it consists of layers of stone, gravel and sand, with the coarsest medium at the bottom and the sand at the top, through which the sewage flows downward.

sanitary sewer. A sewer conveying domestic wastewater containing only a minimum amount of ground water, surface water and industrial wastewater.

saponification. The chemical process of hydrolysis of a fat, usually by an alkali with the formation of glycerol and fatty acid salts. The term was originally used only where the higher fatty acids were involved, forming soaps.

saprobic. Associated with dead and decaying organic matter.

saprobien system. A biological system of classifying degrees of organic pollution, introduced by Kolwitz and Marsson in 1908. Based on the species of organisms present in aquatic communities, the system distinguishes four zones of recovery from gross organic pollution, e.g. (a) polysaprobic; (b) α mesosaprobic; (c) β mesosaprobic; and (d) oligosaprobic. In the polysaprobic zone there is gross organic pollution and the biota are restricted to a few taxa, the individuals of which may, however, be present in high populations. In the mesosaprobic zone oxidation processes are well established, both in water and in bottom sludge. This is subdivided into two zones, α mesosaprobic and β mesosaprobic. In the α mesosaprobic zone there is a high content of amino acids from the breakdown of complex organics. The oxygen content of the water is less than 50 per cent of saturation, although because of the presence of chlorophyll-bearing micro-organisms it fluctuates daily. Macro-organisms are still restricted, and bacterial numbers are high. The β mesosaprobic zone is one of continuing oxidation and mineralization, giving ammoniacal compounds. The oxygen content is never less than 50 per cent of saturation and there is a greater diversity of plant and animal life, with a reduction in the numbers of bacteria. In the oligosaprobic zone there is complete oxidation and mineralization, the water is clear and rich in oxygen and the sludge is almost completely oxidized. There are few bacteria but a wide range of plants and animals, including fish.

saprophytic. Feeding osmotrophically on decaying organic matter.

saprozoic. Feeding phagotrophically on decaying organic matter.

saturation constant (K_S). The concentration of limiting substrate at which the specific bacterial growth rate is one half of the maximum specific growth rate. (This is the application by Monod of Michaelis-Menton kinetics to bacterial growth.)

saveall. Used in paper making for removing fibre and suspended solids from the 'backwater' involving sedimentation, flotation, filtration or centrifugal separation.

scanner. In computer technology, a device which automatically checks on the state of a process or the physical conditions.

schmutzdecke. The living organisms, accumulated debris and detritis of the surface layer of a slow sand filter. Considered to form the effective filtering zone.

scintillation counter. A device for detecting and recording the presence of ionizing radiation, using a scintillator for producing light flashes which are converted into electrical pulses.

scouring organisms. Organisms such as worms, insect larvae and other invertebrate animals which remove the zoogloeal film on the surfaces of the medium in a biological filter, either by feeding activity or by dislodging it. *See* **grazing fauna**.

scouring velocity. *See* **self-cleansing velocity**.

scraper. A power-driven device used in a primary sedimentation tank or a secondary settlement tank for sweeping sludge to a hopper or channel from which it is discharged at intervals. *See* **chain scraper, fixed-bridge scraper, flight scraper, ring-type scraper, rope-hauled scraper blade, rotating half-bridge scraper, travelling-bridge scraper, V-blade scraper with multiple draw-offs**.

screen. A device for removing gross solids from sewage. *See* **band screen, bar screen, cage screen, coarse screen, Discreen, disk screen, drum screen, fine screen, milli-screen**.

screenings. The gross solids in sewage intercepted by screens and removed manually or by raking mechanisms. The quantity depends on the bar spacing and ranges from 0.01 to 0.03m³/d per 1000 population. Screenings weigh between 600 and 900kg/m³ and have a dry solids content of from 10 to 20 per cent, the dry solids containing from 80 to 90 per cent of organic and volatile matter and a calorific value of approximately 15 kJ/kg DS. Unwashed screenings usually have a foul odour and are objectionable in appearance.

screenings dewatering. Debris washed onto screens at the inlet to a sewage works is an obnoxious material difficult to dispose of in its raw state. Since the introduction of fine screens in the mid-1980's, the volume for disposal has doubled and highlighted the need for treatment. Dewatering by pressing and compaction, often in conjunction with disintegration, produces a cleaner material, lower in volume and more easily transported to the disposal point.

screenings disintegrator. A machine evolved from the stereophagus pump which grinds or shreds the gross solids in crude sewage. *See* **disintegrator pump**.

screenings incinerator. A kiln in which screenings are incinerated. May consist of a rotating refractory-lined inclined kiln with hot gases from a gas or oil-burner passing through in a countercurrent direction, the ash being discharged from the lower end of the kiln. After leaving the kiln the gases are heated still further to control odour and then pass through a water-purged cyclone before discharge to atmosphere.

screenings press. A hydraulic press used for dewatering screenings .

screezer. A development of the comminutor where the rotating drum becomes a fine screen, its movement transferring debris to one side for subsequent removal.

screw compactor. A machine by which free water is squeezed from the debris removed from the screens at the inlet to a sewage works. The wet debris is deposited onto the screw which operates against a back pressure induced by an inclined discharge or a spring tensioned outlet flap. Some variations incorporate a reducing pitch screw to promote the squeezing action.

screw pump. A pump used for lifting sewage or sludge, introduced into the UK from Holland about 1965. It consists of an inclined shaft carrying a helix of considerable diameter, which is rotated with little clearance in a circular or semicircular conduit. Sometimes termed an 'Archimedean screw pump'.

screwdown valve. *See* **gate valve**.

scrubber liquor. Liquor containing dissolved and suspended impurities washed from a gas during passage through a scrubber.

scum. A layer of fats, oils, grease and soaps together with particles of plastics, plastics wrapping materials and sludge which has risen to the surface owing to gasification, and which collects on the surface of primary sedimentation tanks and anaerobic digesters.

scum baffle. A plate or board which dips below the surface of sedimentation tanks to prevent scum flowing out with the effluent. Also termed a 'scum board'.

scum board. *See* **scum baffle**.

scum trough. A trough placed in or at the side of a primary sedimentation tank to receive scum.

scum weir. A weir the crest of which may be lowered to enable scum to be withdrawn from a primary sedimentation tank. Also termed a 'skimming weir'.

sea fisheries committee. A committee set up under the Sea Fisheries Regulation Act 1888 to protect and regulate sea fisheries, with power to make by-laws for prohibiting or regulating the deposit or discharge of any solid or liquid substance detrimental to sea fish or sea fishing.

seak tank. A tank in which the acid cracking of wool-scouring liquor takes place, involving the addition of sulphuric acid to the liquor to neutralize alkalinity and separate grease.

secondary digestion tank. *See* **digestion tank**.

secondary settlement tank. A tank through which the effluent from biological filters or an activated-sludge plant flows for the purpose of separating settleable solids.

secondary sludge. Solid matter in the effluent from a biological filter or an activated-sludge plant which has been deposited as sludge in secondary settlement tanks.

secondary treatment. The treatment of sewage, usually after the removal of suspended solids, by bacteria under aerobic conditions during which organic matter in solution is oxidized or incorporated into cells which may be removed by settlement. This may be achieved by biological filtration or by the activated-sludge process. Sometimes termed 'aerobic biological treatment'.

sedimentation. The process by which settleable solids are removed from sewage by passing it through a tank at such a velocity that the solids gravitate to the floor to form sludge.

sedimentation/flow-balancing tank. A specially designed horizontal- or radial-flow sedimentation tank, which fulfils the dual function of sedimentation and flow balancing.

sedimentation/storm-sewage tank. A storm-sewage tank which is used as a horizontal-flow sedimentation tank in dry weather.

sedimentation tank. A tank in which sewage is retained for a sufficient period and at the same time is flowing at a sufficiently low velocity for a portion of the solids to be removed by gravity.

seeding. The inoculation of a biological system for the purpose of introducing favourable organisms, e.g. (a) the return of activated sludge or of biological-filter effluent containing humus to mix with sewage prior to biological treatment; (b) the seeding of undigested sludge with sludge that is undergoing digestion to accelerate the initial stages of decomposition; or (c) the seeding of sterile samples in the BOD test.

self-cleansing velocity. The minimum velocity (> 0.8 m/s) in a sewer necessary to keep solids in suspension and prevent their deposition, with the consequent possibility of blockages or of the production of a foul odour due to decomposition.

self-purification. The process whereby polluting materials discharged to a natural water are removed by physico-chemical and biological agencies.

sensor. A device which gives an output or undergoes a reversible physical change directly attributable to a particular cause, which can detect such substances as ammonia, dissolved oxygen or suspended solids, or monitor temperature or pressure.

separate system. A sewerage system in which foul sewage and surface water are conveyed in separate pipes.

separating weir. *See* **storm-sewage diversion weir**.

septic. A condition produced by lack of dissolved oxygen and oxidised nitrogen (nitrate or nitrite). Putrefaction can occur.

septic tank. A type of sedimentation tank in which the sludge is retained sufficiently long for the organic content to undergo anaerobic digestion. When sludge is eventually removed, some is left in the tank to act as a 'seed' to initiate further digestion. Used for receiving the sewage from houses and other premises which are too isolated for connection to a foul sewer. cf. **cesspit**.

septicity. The tendency for sewage to become stale or septic due to lack of dissolved oxygen and oxidised nitrogen (nitrate or nitrite) and (a) passage through long flat sewers; (b) extremely warm weather; (c) the presence of slime growths; or (d) its high sulphate content; when anaerobic decomposition of organic matter takes place and a foul odour may develop.

sequestration. A dated term which refers to the ability of a complexing agent, which in this context is almost invariably a chelating agent, to 'lock up' a metal ion and prevent it from taking part in chemical reactions, e.g. the sequestration of calcium to prevent scum formation with soap. *See* **complex, complexing agent, chelating agent**.

servomechanism. A mechanism which controls the movement of another, independently powered, mechanism, the output power being much larger than, but proportional to, the input power. Usually includes a feedback device in which a signal indicating any deviation is amplified and used in initiating corrective action.

seston. Living and non-living bodies or parts of organisms drifting in water.

settleable solids. Suspended solids which will settle in sewage or sewage effluent during (a) the nominal retention period of a sedimentation tank or settlement tank; or (b) a period of quiescence of 2 hours under laboratory conditions.

settled sewage. Sewage from which the gross solids and most of the settleable solids have been removed by settlement.

settlement tank. *See* **secondary settlement tank**.

settling tank. *See* **sedimentation tank**.

sewage. The water-borne wastes of a community. Domestic sewage is derived from a residential area. An industrial sewage is from a mixed residential and industrial area. Storm sewage is that flowing to a treatment works in wet weather or discharged from storm overflows, when the sewage is diluted to a greater or lesser extent with rainwater.

sewage fungus. A macroscopic plumose slime growth of heterotrophic micro-organisms which grow in organically polluted waters. The organisms are usually bacteria, e.g. *Sphaerotilus*, *Zoogloea*, or protozoa, e.g. *Carchesium*. Sometimes true fungi such as *Leptomitus* and *Geotrichum* are found.

sewage-treatment works. A term for the structures, plant and equipment used for treating sewage and sludge and for pumping on site. Also termed a 'sewage works', 'sewage disposal works', 'water pollution control works', 'water reclamation works', 'wastewater treatment works'.

sewage works. *See* **sewage-treatment works**.

sewer. A pipe conveying wastewater discharged into it from two or more house drains being the property of a drainage company or authority. *See* **egg-shaped sewer, foul sewer, intercepting sewer, lateral sewer, outfall sewer, private sewer, public sewer, relief sewer, sanitary sewer, tank sewer, trunk sewer.**

sewerage. A system of pipes and appurtenances for the collection and transportation of domestic and industrial wastewaters.

Sheffield system. See paddle-aeration system.

Shigella. A bacterium responsible for bacillary dysentery and common in polluted waters.

Shone ejector. *See* **pneumatic ejector.**

short-circuiting. The hydraulic conditions in parts of a tank where the time of travel is less than the flow-through period, or the nominal retention period.

side water depth. The depth from water level to the bottom of the vertical peripheral wall of a radial-flow or upward-flow tank.

side-weir overflow. A weir constructed along the length of the sewer. When the crest of the weir is below the level of the horizontal diameter of the upstream pipe it is called a 'low side-weir overflow'; when above it is called a 'high side-weir overflow'.

Sieger detector. A proprietary make of fixed gas detector lamp consisting of a low voltage supply, a control unit and a detector head. The detector head contains two filaments, one catalysed and the other not, and these are connected with a potentiometer to form a Wheatstone bridge circuit. This is initially balanced by the slider of the potentiometer, and when the ambient temperature changes the resistances of both filaments change in the same proportion and no signal is given. Combustion of methane on the catalysed filament causes the resistance to change, when out-of-balance current flows. This is amplified by a transistor circuit to operate a relay which is connected to an alarm system.

silage. Silage is green fodder to which molasses has usually been added so that, when stored in a silo, it ferments and is preserved for winter use as cattle food. Liquor draining from it is exceptionally strong and production is seasonal.

silk boiling. This involves the following processes: (a) boiling of raw silk in a series of soap solutions to remove natural gum (sericin); (b) rinsing in tepid water rendered slightly alkaline by addition of sodium carbonate; (c) washing in cold water. Wastewaters include water used in boiling and washwaters.

sill. The crest of a rectangular weir or other weir structure.

Simater sand filter. *See* **horizontal-flow sand filter.**

simazine. Non-agricultural herbicide used in weed control. *See* **triazine.**

Simcar aerator. A trade name for a mechanical surface aerator which draws a mixture of sewage and activated sludge from below and distributes it with intense disturbance over the surface of an aeration tank.

Simplex aerator. *See* **cone aerator.**

Simplex surface-aeration system. A trade name for a method of mechanical surface aeration used in the activated-sludge process, developed by J. Bolton and first used at Bury in 1920. A mixture of sewage and activated sludge flows through a rectangular tank and is circulated and aerated by a series of specially-designed aerators which draw the mixture usually through an uptake tube and distribute it with intense disturbance over the surface.

single-stage filtration. The conventional method of applying biological filtration, in which settled sewage passes through a single filter once only. A single-stage filter may be used for treating (a) settled sewage at low rates to yield a 'Royal Commission Effluent'; (b) comminuted crude sewage or crude sewage from which gross solids and grit have been removed (when the process is termed 'extended filtration'); (c) the effluent from a partial-treatment activated-sludge plant; (d) the effluent from an activated-sludge plant at a high rate to produce a highly nitrified effluent (when the filter is termed a 'nitrifying filter'); or (e) settled sewage at a high rate to produce a partially-oxidized effluent (when the process is termed 'high-rate treatment'). A single-stage filter may also be used for treating (a) a mixture of settled sewage and recirculated settled effluent (termed 'effluent recirculation'); (b) a mixture of settled sewage and settled effluent from other filters (termed 'pseudo-recirculation'); or (c) the effluent from an activated-sludge plant at a high rate to produce a highly nitrified effluent which is returned to the inlet of the activated-sludge plant to mix with settled sewage being fed to the plant (when the filter is termed a 'cyclo-nitrifying filter'). *See* **extended-filtration process, high-rate filter, nitrifying filter, single-stage filtration with effluent recirculation**.

single-stage filtration with effluent recirculation. The application to a single-stage biological filter of a mixture of settled sewage and recirculated settled effluent, e.g. in a ratio of 1:1. *See* **single stage filtration, recirculation**.

sinuous flow. *See* **turbulent flow**.

siphon. A pipe or other conduit, typically in the shape of an inverted U, a portion of which lies above the hydraulic gradient. It follows that any liquid in that portion is at a pressure less than atmospheric and hence a partial vacuum has to be created to start a flow of liquid through the siphon. *See* **inverted siphon**.

siphon overflow. An overflow where siphon pipes or ducts are used instead of a weir to discharge excess storm sewage.

Sirofloc process. A trade name for a patented water-treatment process using magnetite to remove colour, turbidity, iron and aluminium from water. The magnetite is regenerated with caustic soda solution resulting in a highly alkaline wastewater.

skimming. The process of removing floating grease or scum from the surface of sewage in a sedimentation tank.

skimming tank. A small specially-designed tank through which a domestic or an industrial wastewater passes and in which oil and grease separate so that they can be skimmed off. *See* **interceptor**.

slate bed. A modification of the contact bed, introduced by W. J. Dibdin in 1903, in which crude sewage was applied on a fill-and-draw system to a bed filled with horizontal layers of slates separated by distance pieces. When the bed was filled with sewage, sludge was deposited on the slates and this was 'digested' during the time the bed was standing empty. The digested sludge was then flushed out with water before the bed was refilled with crude sewage.

slaughterhouse or abattoir wastes. Wastewaters from a slaughterhouse or abattoir include faeces and urine, blood, undigested food from paunches of slaughtered animals, and washings from carcasses, floor and utensils.

sleek. *See* **slick**.

slick. A patch of material, e.g. oil or scum, floating on the surface of the sea, or other body of water, created by the discharge of domestic or industrial wastewater. Also termed 'sleek'.

sloughing. A phenomenon which occurs in a biological filter during the spring, when with the warmer weather the scouring organisms return to the surface layer of medium and feed on growths which have accumulated during the winter and may have caused ponding. It may also occur at other times after ponding has been relieved. At such times a greatly increased amount of suspended matter is discharged from the filter with the effluent.

slow sand filter. A sand filter used for removing suspended solids from (1) biologically-treated sewage, the water passing downward through a layer of sand on coarser material and thus into underdrains, whilst the filter is cleaned at intervals by removing the surface layer and replacing it with fresh sand, (2) potable water as a treatment method where the schmutzdecke provides the biological system to assimilate organic matter, both suspended and dissolved.

sludge. A mixture of solids and water produced during the treatment of wastewater. **See activated sludge, chemically-precipitated sludge, commercially dry sludge, digested sludge, humus sludge, liquid sludge, mixed sludge, primary sludge, raw sludge, returned activated sludge, rising sludge, secondary sludge, surplus activated sludge**.

sludge age. The number of days over which the total mass of sludge wasted (assumed to be at a constant rate) is equal to the mass of sludge undergoing aeration when an activated-sludge plant is operated at equilibrium conditions. It is calculated by dividing the mass of sludge in the aeration tanks by the mass of sludge wasted per day including the suspended solids discharged with the effluent daily. The reciprocal of sludge age is termed the 'specific growth rate' of sludge.

sludge blanket level. The upper surface of the mass of sludge in a sedimentation tank, clarifier or thickener.

sludge cake. Sludge that has been dewatered to the extent that it can be handled as a solid, containing usually more than 20 per cent dry solids depending on the type of sludge and method of dewatering.

sludge conditioning. *See* **conditioning**.

sludge density index (SDI). Proposed by W. Donaldson in the USA in 1932, this is a measure of the settleability of activated sludge. Calculated as follows:

$$SDI = \frac{\text{suspended solids (per cent)} \times 100}{\text{settled volume of sludge (per cent) after 30 min}}$$

Varies from about 2.0 for a sludge which settles readily to about 0.3 for one which has a poor settleability. The reciprocal of the sludge volume index (SVI) multiplied by 100. *See* **sludge volume index**.

sludge dewatering. The removal of water from sludge by drainage or filtration under pressure with the production of a cake containing usually more than 20 per cent of dry solids.

sludge digestion. *See* **anaerobic digestion.**

sludge-drying bed. An underdrained shallow lagoon into which liquid sludge is discharged to a depth generally less than 300 mm so that dewatering takes place, partly by drainage and partly by evaporation. In some cases provision is made for decanting surface water.

sludge freezing process. A process for dewatering sludge by freezing with or without the addition of a chemical. Studied at the Northern Works of the London County Council from 1948 to 1953, and since applied elsewhere for dewatering waterworks sludge.

sludge gas. The gas evolved during anaerobic digestion of sludge. Usually contains about 70 per cent methane and 30 per cent carbon dioxide by volume, with traces of nitrogen, hydrogen and hydrogen sulphide. Its calorific value ranges from 22 to 26 kJ/m^3.

sludge growth index. The weight of sludge produced per unit weight of BOD applied to an activated-sludge plant.

sludge level detector. A device for locating the upper surface of settled sludge in a sedimentation tank, depending on the interruption by the sludge of light passing from a source on to a photoelectric cell.

sludge liquor. *See* **liquor.**

sludge loading. The weight of BOD applied to an activated-sludge plant per day per unit weight of activated sludge under aeration.

sludge pressing. *See* **pressure filtration.**

sludge producer. Any person who manages a plant at which sludge is produced for disposal. (ref. The Sludge (Use in Agriculture) Regulations 1989.)

sludge production. The amount of sludge produced from sewage in terms of cubic metres per head per annum, kilogrammes of dry solids or volatile matter per head per day, or kg of dry solids per kg BOD removed (or applied) per day.

sludge return ratio. In an activated-sludge plant, the ratio of the rate at which sludge is returned to the aeration tanks from the secondary settlement tanks to the average rate of flow of sewage through the plant, expressed as a percentage.

sludge solids balance. The relationship between the weight of dry settleable solids entering a sewage-treatment works or sludge-treatment process and the weights of dry solids leaving the works or process as sludge or liquor, or in the final effluent.

sludge treatment. The processing of sludge to render it suitable for disposal. It may include one or more of the following processes: digestion, conditioning, dewatering, drying, and incineration.

sludge utilization. The utilization of sludge, e.g. in horticulture or agriculture, in either liquid or solid form or after composting with household refuse.

sludge volume index (SVI). Introduced by F.W. Mohlman in the USA in 1934 as a rough measure of sludge settleability. It is defined as the volume in millilitres occupied by 1 gramme of activated sludge after settling the aerated liquor for 30 minutes thus:

$$SVI = \frac{\text{settled volume of sludge (per cent) after 30 min}}{\text{suspended solids (per cent)}}$$

The mixed liquor is usually settled quiescently in a 1-litre measuring cylinider. For a typical liquor containing 3000mg/l suspended solids, SVIs of 50 and 200 would indicate good and poor settling characteristics respectively. As the SVI is apparently dependent in an unpredictable way on the concentration of suspended solids in the liquor, it is preferable to quote both figures together. The SVI is also dependent on a number of other factors, such as the diameter of the measuring cylinder, the depth of sludge, and the degree of turbulence. As conditions in a full-scale tank are always 'turbulent', for tank design it is preferable to measure the SVI in a cylinder equipped with a slow-speed (1 rev/min) stirrer. *See* **rate of hindered settling, sludge density index**.

sludge yield. The rate of dewatering sludge in terms of kilogrammes of dry solids per square metre of filter surface per hour or the rate of production of micro-organisms per unit mass of BOD removed daily.

sluice valve. *See* **gate valve**.

small sewage-treatment works. A works treating sewage of a domestic character from small groups of houses and from individual establishments, e.g. country houses, schools, institutions, factories and similar buildings containing up to 350 persons.

soak. Pit containing water in which skins are immersed to remove dung, blood, etc., before tanning.

soda ash. A common name for commercial anhydrous sodium carbonate.

soda process. Process used for manufacturing pulp from wood in which the wood is digested under pressure in a solution of sodium hydroxide, the spent lye being concentrated and incinerated for recovery of soda.

soffit. The top of the arch inside a sewer or other conduit. Sometimes termed the 'crown', but this usually refers to the outside top of a sewer. *See* **invert**.

soft detergent. A synthetic detergent which is readily oxidized biologically, at least 90 per cent of a typical soft detergent being removed from sewage during normal treatment. Examples are linear alkyl benzene sulphonates (LAS) and ethyloxylated long-chain alcohols. *See* **hard detergent**.

soft water. Water which forms an immediate lather with soap and has a total hardness which is typically less than 60 milligrammes per litre (as $CaCO_3$).

soil injection. A method of utilising sewage sludge on agricultural land by injecting it below the surface of the soil at a controlled rate.

solenoid-operated valve. A valve actuated by a soft iron plunger in a solenoid, used in remote control systems.

solute. A substance dissolved in a solvent to form a solution.

solvent. A substance, usually a liquid, used for dissolving other substances.

Soxhlet extraction apparatus. A laboratory apparatus for extraction of the soluble portion of a substance, e.g. grease from acidified dry sludge, by continuous circulation of boiling solvent through it.

sparger. A non-porous diffuser producing large bubbles of air, used in an activated-sludge plant.

species. Biologically, organisms forming a natural population and which transmit specific characteristics from parent to offspring. Reproductively isolated from other populations.

specific gravity. The ratio of the mass of a given volume of a substance to the mass of an equal volume of water at a temperature of 4°C.

specific growth rate. *See* **sludge age**.

specific ion electrode. A term which was used to describe electrodes which responded to specific ions. Now known that they are not specific and term replaced by 'ion selective electrode'. *See* **ion selective electrode**.

specific resistance to filtration. The resistance of a unit weight of sludge cake per unit area at a given pressure, defined by the equation:

$$r = 2bPA^2 /Cn$$

where P is the filtration pressure (normally 49 kPa), A is the area of filtration (cm^2), C is the weight of dry cake solids per unit volume of unfiltered sludge (g), and n is the viscosity of the filtrate. The term b is given by the equation $\theta/V = bV + a$ where V is the volume of filtrate (ml) in time θ, and a is a constant. The specific resistance to filtration is expressed in terms of m/kg at 49 kPa. This concept was introduced by Dr. P. Coackley in 1955. *See* **capillary suction time, pressure filtration time**.

specific speed. As applied to centrifugal pumps, the specific speed forms a basis for comparison, as regards angular velocity, between different designs of impeller. With a pump of known performance, it is the speed (rev/min) which a geometrically similar impeller would acquire in order to deliver 1 litre per second under a head of 1 metre, a coefficient of 0.1155 being included to allow for metrication.

specific surface area. The total surface area per unit volume of medium used in a biological filter, expressed in terms of square metres per cubic metre.

spent lees. In the manufacture of whisky, the residue from the second distillation of the fermented liquor.

spent liquor. Liquor produced when crude ammoniacal liquor from the distillation of coal is distilled in a current of steam. Although much weaker than ammoniacal liquor, it is still highly polluting.

spent wash. In the manufacture of whisky, spent wash is the residue from the first distillation of the fermented liquor; it is also known as 'pot ale' or 'burnt ale'.

Sphaerotilus. A filamentous bacterium of the order Chlamydobacteriaceae, which may form plumose growths in polluted waters known as 'sewage fungus' and when present in activated sludge is associated with bulking.

Spiralarm lamp. A proprietary make of gas detector lamp burning paraffin oil at a wick which can be adjusted to produce a flame of definite height, predetermined by a fixed pointer. In an atmosphere containing an inflammable gas the flame height increases and the temperature of a flat metal spiral is thereby raised, which causes it to unwind and complete the electrical circuit of a red warning lamp. The lamp will detect 2 per cent of methane in air. Hydrogen sulphide is detected by means of a lead acetate paper attached to the lamp.

spiral-flow aeration. A method of aeration used in the activated-sludge process in which air diffusers are located along one side of the aeration tank to produce a spiral or helical motion of the mixed liquor.

splash plate. *See* **spreader plate**.

spores. Highly specialized reproductive cells of fungi, algae and protozoa.

spot sample. *See* **grab sample**.

spray dryer. A form of dryer in which the liquid sludge is sprayed or atomized into a hot chamber.

spray gun. *See* **rain-gun**.

spray irrigation. The irrigation of arable land or grassland by means of sewage or liquid sludge emerging from apparatus designed or adapted to eject liquid into the air in the form of jets or spray.

spreader plate. A specially shaped plate fixed under each orifice in the distributor arm of a biological filter to spread the settled sewage evenly over the surface of the filter.

spring rising. *See* **filter unloading**.

sprinkler. *See* **distributor**.

squeegee. A device, generally with a soft rubber edge, used for pushing sludge deposited in a sedimentation tank to the sludge outlet.

stability. The ability of a wastewater, either before or after treatment, to resist putrefaction.

stability test. A test for biologically-treated sewage in which methylene blue is added to a sample of the effluent, the time taken to decolorize the dye being a measure of the stability of the effluent. Also termed the 'methylene blue test', 'incubator test'.

stabilization pond. A large shallow basin used for the stabilization of organic matter in crude or settled sewage. Also termed an 'oxidation pond'.

stage treatment. Treatment in which a similar process takes place in more than one stage, as with two-stage sedimentation, two-stage biological filtration, and primary and secondary digestion.

standard-rate filtration. Biological filtration in which the hydraulic loading is within the range 0.3 to 0.6 cubic metre per cubic metre of medium per day, and the BOD loading is within the range 0.08 to 0.12 kilogramme per cubic metre of medium per day.

standard solution. In volumetric analysis, a solution of known concentration.

standby plant. Plant which is available for use in an emergency.

standing-wave flume. A Venturi flume with a free discharge and a sub-critical velocity downstream so that a hydraulic jump or standing wave is formed. The following formula gives the rate of discharge:
$$Q = 1.71 \; BH^{1.5},$$
where Q is the rate of discharge (m^3/s), B the width of the throat of the flume (m), and H is the head in the approach channel over the invert of the throat of the flume (m). *See* **Venturi flume**.

static head. *See* **head**.

stationary distributor. A biological-filter distributor no part of which moves from point to point, e.g. fixed-jet distributor. *See* **fixed-jet distributor**, **perforated-pipe distributor**.

stearine amine. *See* **amine treatment**.

stepped aeration. A modification of the activated-sludge process proposed by

T.R. Haseldine of the USA in 1937. Using diffused air, the intensity of aeration is varied according to the oxygen demand of the mixture of sewage and activated sludge (mixed liquor), more air being added per square metre of floor area at the inlet end of the aeration tank than at the outlet end. Also applicable to surface aeration by varying the depth of immersion of the aerator. Also termed 'tapered aeration'.

stepped feeding. A modification of the activated-sludge process introduced by R.H. Gould in New York in 1939 in which portions of the settled sewage are fed as increments along the length of the aeration tank or channel, the whole of the returned activated sludge entering at the inlet end. It was anticipated that by this means the demand for oxygen would be maintained fairly uniform throughout the tank but it is now accepted that it achieved load distribution. Also termed 'incremental loading'.

stepped loading. *See* **stepped feeding**.

Stereophagus pump. A special type of centrifugal pump introduced into the UK by J. Björnsted in 1927, used for pumping crude sewage or sludge and equipped with a cutting blade for disintegrating gross solids.

sterilization. The destruction of living organisms by heat, chlorination, ozonation, or ultraviolet radiation.

stilling-pond overflow. A chamber designed with the object of reducing the amount of turbulence in the vicinity of an overflow. The overflow arrangement may consist of a weir or weirs at the sides or end of the chamber; alternately, siphons may be used to discharge the excess storm sewage.

stirred specific volume index (SSVI). A sludge settling index produced from a stirring apparatus designed by the Water Research Centre. It is the volume calculated to be occupied by 1 gramme of sludge after 30 minutes settlement in a gently stirred cylinder (50 cm deep and 10 cm diameter) when mixed liquor from an activated-sludge plant with a suspended solids concentration of 3.5 g/l is initially added to the cylinder. Normally two tests are conducted with solids concentration above and below 3.5 g/l and then the value at 3.5 g/l calculated. The gentle stirring is to minimise the effects of the cylinder walls on the rate of hindered settlement.

Stokes' Law. A law applying to the settlement of fine granular particles in a liquid in a quiescent state, the settling velocity depending on the size, shape and density of the particles, and the density and viscosity of the liquid in which it is suspended, thus:

$$V = \frac{2\,gr^2}{9n} \cdot (D_s - D_1)$$

where V is the velocity of the particle (m/s), D_S is the density of the particle (kg/m^3), r is the radius of the particle (m), n is the viscosity of the liquid (kg/m s), D_1 is the density of the liquid (kg/m^3), and g is the acceleration due to gravity (m/s^2).

storm overflow. A device on a combined or partially-separate sewerage system, introduced for the purpose of relieving the system of flows in excess of a selected rate, the excess flow being discharged, possibly after removal of gross solids, to a convenient receiving water.

storm sewage. *See* **sewage**.

storm-sewage diversion weir. A weir, usually located upstream of the primary sedimentation tanks, over which in wet weather is diverted all storm sewage reaching the treatment works in excess of that which is to receive biological treatment. The proportion receiving full treatment is usually controlled by an electrically-operated penstock operating in conjunction with a flow recorder downstream of the penstock. Excess flow is diverted to storm-sewage tanks.

storm-sewage tank. A tank into which, in wet weather, is diverted all the sewage and rainwater reaching a treatment works in excess of that which is to receive biological treatment. Its purpose is to store as much of the storm sewage as possible, for return to the works inlet after the flow has returned to normal, and to remove settleable solids from the remainder which overflows from the tank to a receiving water.

storm water. *See* **sewage**.

stormwater tank. *See* **storm-sewage tank**.

straining filter. A layer of charcoal, gravel or coke used in the early days of sewage treatment for removing solids from crude sewage. cf. **roughing filter**.

stratification. Stratification in a sedimentation tank is caused by a liquor of different density, such as a warm liquor or one containing a high concentration of salt or activated sludge, entering the tank and continuing as a separate layer instead of mixing with the tank contents. *See* **thermal stratification**.

streamline flow. *See* **laminar flow**.

strength. *See* **McGowan strength**.

Streptococcus faecalis. A bacterial indicator of faecal contamination of water.

stuffing box. A recess, filled with packing fitting tightly round the spindle of a centrifugal pump or the piston rod of a reciprocating pump to prevent the leakage of liquid from the pump or of air into it.

submarine pipeline. A long pipeline laid on the sea-bed and terminating in one or more outlets for conveying wastewater to sea for disposal. Also termed a marine outfall.

submerged biological aerated filter. (SBAF). A form of biological filtration where the medium is completely immersed in an aerated stream of settled sewage to achieve biochemical treatment by micro-organisms growing on the surfaces of the medium. Depending on the particular type of commercial process, the flow may go down through the bed with dense media (such as shale or anthracite) or up through the bed with buoyant media (plastics) retained below a suitable mesh.

submerged weir. A weir in which the level of the water downstream is higher than the sill. Such a weir is often used at the inlet of a horizontal-flow tank. Also termed a 'drowned weir'.

submersible pump. An electrically-driven centrifugal pump which can be lowered into a wet well as a complete unit and operated whilst completely submerged in the liquid being pumped, thereby saving the cost of a separate dry well.

subsoil. The layer of material between the surface soil and the bed-rock below.

substrate. 1. A substance which is being changed in a reaction controlled by enzymes, normally in viable organisms. 2. The liquid portion of the mixed liquor in an activated-sludge plant.

substratum. The solid bottom material of a river or lake to which the benthic organisms are either attached or with which they are associated, e.g. mud, rock, stones, cf. **substrate**.

sub-surface float. A body which is submerged to a known depth and used for measuring the velocity or the direction of the flow at that depth. Usually attached by a line to a surface float which indicates its position; it is then termed a 'double float'. *See* **surface float, velocity rod**.

sub-surface irrigation. A system by which settled sewage is disposed of by running it into lines of open-jointed field tiles laid in trenches about 0.6 metre deep and surrounded by clinker or other medium. Where the soil is not very porous two lines of field tiles may be used, one above the other with a layer of coarse sand between them, effluent from the lower line discharging into a receiving water.

suction dredger. A pump mounted on a travelling gantry and used for sucking grit from a grit channel for discharge into a trough or screw conveyor.

suction pipe. The pipe through which a pump draws the liquid to be pumped.

suction valve. A check valve on the suction side of a centrifugal pump.

suction well. *See* **wet well**.

suds. An aqueous emulsion of soluble oil used as a cutting oil in engineering works, as distinct from a neat oil.

suint. *See* **yolk**.

sulphate process. Process used for manufacturing pulp from wood in which the wood is digested with a solution containing a mixture of sodium salts, including the hydroxide, sulphate and sulphide.

sulphide. *See* **hydrogen sulphide**.

sulphide dyeing. Application of a sulphide dye to cotton or other vegetable fibres in a solution containing sodium sulphide and alkali. Wastewaters include spent liquor and rinsing waters.

sulphite process. Process used for manufacturing pulp from wood in which the wood is digested with a solution of calcium sulphite.

sulphur cycle. The cycle of processes by which sulphur and its compounds are utilized and transformed in nature.

sump well. *See* **wet well**.

supernatant liquor. The liquor in a sedimentation tank or settlement tank, or a sludge digestion tank, lying between the deposited solids and any floating scum.

supervisory process control. Advanced techniques for controlling a continuous-flow process, including automatic set point control, cascade control, ratio control, programme control, and sequence control. These require specialized equipment or specially adapted conventional controllers, with a digital computer being used to superimpose the overall plant requirement on to individual controllers. *See* **process control techniques**.

suppressed weir. *See* **rectangular weir**.

surcharge. A condition obtaining when the flow in a sewer increases after it is already flowing full.

surface-active agent. A wetting agent which, by reducing the surface tension of a liquid, improves the wetting action. It is the essential constituent of a detergent formulation and is commonly abbreviated to 'surfactant'. *See* **surfactant**.

surface aeration. Aeration by mechanically agitating the surface of the mixed liquor in an activated-sludge plant and at the same time causing vertical mixing of the body of liquid. Surface aerators include brush aerators, cage rotors, cone aerators, Mammoth aerators and paddle aerators.

surface float. A body floating on the water surface and used for measuring the surface velocity or determining the direction of flow. *See* **sub-surface float**, **velocity rod**.

surface irrigation. *See* **land treatment**.

surface loading. The maximum rate of flow to be treated per day per unit area, or:

$$\text{Surface loading } (\text{m}^3/\text{m}^2 \text{ d}) = \frac{\text{maximum flow } (\text{m}^3/\text{d})}{\text{surface area } (\text{m}^2)}$$

It is also termed upward flow velocity.

surface tension. A property possessed by a liquid surface, whereby it appears to be covered by a thin elastic membrane under tension. Measured by the force acting normally across unit length in the surface caused by unbalanced molecular cohesive forces near the surface.

surface water. The run-off from paved and unpaved roads, buildings and land.

surface-water sewer. *See* **separate system**.

surfactant. A contraction of 'surface-active agent'. Surfactants are essential constituents of detergent formulations and include both soap and synthetic materials synthesized from petroleum or natural oils such as coconut oil. *See* **surface-active agent**.

surge. A sudden increase in pressure in a pipeline, e.g. due to the closing of a valve.

surge tank. An open-topped tank at the head of a rising main, its purpose being to mitigate the effect of pressure surges.

surge vessel. *See* **air chamber**.

surplus activated sludge. That portion of the activated sludge separated from the mixed liquor in secondary settlement tanks which is surplus to requirements.

surveillance. The repeated and standardized measurement of a variable in order that a trend in time may be detected. Biological surveillance is surveillance applied to detect ecological changes in the flora and fauna of rivers or estuaries.

survey. A biological or chemical survey is an exercise carried out to establish a pattern of spatial variation at one point in time.

suspended solids. In sewage analysis, those solids retained after filtration either through a glass fibre filter paper followed by washing and drying at 105°C, or by centrifugation followed by washing and removal of the supernatant liquid.

Sylvicola fenestralis. A dipterous fly whose larvae are common grazers in biological filters. The adults may cause a nuisance when they leave the filters. Formerly *Anisopus fenestralis*.

symbiosis. The intimate association of two dissimilar organisms from which each organism benefits, e.g. the association of nitrogen-fixing bacteria with leguminous plants.

synaeresis. The spontaneous expulsion of liquid from a gel.

synecology. Ecology of a community. cf. **autecology**.

synergism. The increase in efficiency or intensity of a physiological process or behaviour pattern of an organism due to stimulation by another organism in the vicinity.

synthetic detergent. A product the formulation of which is specially devised to promote the development of detergency. Derived from petroleum, there being three main classes: (a) anionic detergents, which ionize in water to give an active anion which is responsible for the detergent action; (b) non-ionic detergents, which do not ionize in water; (c) cationic detergents, in which the cation is the active part of the molecule. Commercial detergents contain from 15 to 35 per cent surface-active matter, the remainder including 'builders' and substances which prevent dirt from being re-deposited during laundering or increase foaming.

synthetic resin. A man-made resin, prepared by polymerization and used as plastics, varnish, in adhesives and in ion exchange, and as a plastics medium in biological filters.

Système International des Unités. *See* **International System of Units**.

T

TAD. *See* **thermophilic aerobic digestion**.

Taenia. A genus of parasitic tapeworm of the class Cestoda, the eggs of which are dispersed through sewage and polluted waters.

tank. A large container in which a liquid or sludge is retained for a period or through which it is passing continuously. *See* **aeration tank, balancing tank, chemical solution tank, constant-head tank, detritus tank, digestion tank, Dortmund tank, fill-and-draw tank, horizontal-flow tank, Imhoff tank, radial-flow tank, seak tank, secondary settlement tank, sedimentation/ flow-balancing tank, sedimentation/storm-sewage tank, sedimentation tank, septic tank, skimming tank, storm-sewage tank, thickening tank, two-storey tank**.

tank sewer. A length of sewer of enlarged cross-section used for storing sewage at peak flows, during periods when pumps are not in operation, or during periods of high tide.

tanker. A vehicle used for conveying liquids such as liquid sludge.

tanning. Conversion of skins of animals into leather, involving the following principal processes: (a) soaking skins in water to remove dung, blood, etc.; (b) softening and loosening hair by immersion in milk of lime to which an accelerator may have been added, this usually being sodium sulphide; (c) removal of hair by scraping; (d) de-liming, the method depending on the type of skins being dealt with and the method of tanning; (e) bating; (f) tanning by immersion in solutions of tanning liquor, sometimes the solutions being of increasing strength and sometimes (particularly with light leathers) a single bath being used; (g) finishing, involving treatment with an emulsion of sulphonated oil in water, or impregnation with oils and greases. Wastewaters include wastes from the preliminary processes (a) to (e), termed 'beam-house wastes', and wastes from subsequent processes (f) and (g), termed 'tanyard wastes'.

tanyard wastes. Wastewaters produced in a tannery as a result of tanning and finishing the leather.

Tanypus. A genus of chironomid fly the larvae of which are aquatic.

tapered aeration. *See* **stepped aeration**.

taxon. Any definite unit in a classification system of organisms.

Taxa-taxonomic units:

Kingdom	e.g. Metazoa
Phylum	Arthropoda
Class	Insecta
Order	Diptera
Family	Psychodidae
Genus	*Psychoda*
Species	*Psychoda alternata*

In addition, each taxon may be sub-divided.

telescopic bellmouth. A vertical length of pipe with a bellmouth outlet so arranged that the level of the outlet can be raised or lowered by means of a screw operated manually or by electrical power. Used for withdrawing sludge from tanks.

telescopic valve. *See* **decanting valve**.

temporary hardness. Hardness due to bicarbonates of calcium and magnesium that can be removed by boiling, when the bicarbonates are decomposed into insoluble carbonates, carbon dioxide and water. *See* **permanent hardness**.

Tenten filter. A trade name for a proprietary type of continuous-wash, downward-flow sand filter.

teratogenesis. Production of monsters or misshapen organisms; the production of abnormal offspring through somatic injury during development (caused by chemical or physical factors).

tertiary treatment. The further treatment of biologically-treated sewage by removing suspended matter to enable the effluent to comply with a more stringent standard before discharge to a receiving water. Also termed 'polishing'.

textile wastes. Wastewaters produced in connexion with the preparation of wool, cotton, silk, jute and man-made fibres, or during the manufacture of fabrics from them, including scouring, de-sizing, dyeing, printing, bleaching and mercerizing.

thallus. A combination of cells of a plant not differentiated into stem and leaves.

thermal conductivity. The amount of heat transmitted in unit time across unit area of a slab of a substance of unit thickness when the temperature difference between the faces of the slab is 1°C.

thermal drying. The drying of sludge by heating it to above ambient temperature.

thermal pollution. Pollution caused by a heated discharge, e.g. cooling water from a power station.

thermal storage vessel. An insulated vessel containing water which is used for storing waste heat from a dual-fuel engine.

thermal stratification. The stratification of a body of water caused by temperature-induced density differences.

thermocline. The layer in a thermally stratified body of water where the temperature changes rapidly with depth between the upper warm water (epilimnion) and the lower cold water (hypolimnion).

thermocouple. An instrument for measuring temperature, consisting of two dissimilar metallic conductors joined at each end. One junction is at the point where the temperature is to be measured and the other junction is at a lower fixed temperature. The difference in temperature causes a current to flow in the circuit formed by the two conductors which may be measured by a galvanometer. Incorporated in a pyrometer, used for measuring high temperatures, as in a dual-fuel engine or furnace.

thermophilic aerobic digestion (TAD). The aerobic digestion of primary or mixed sludges. Using a specially-designed aerator and reactor, an operating temperature of 55°C can be achieved with heat derived solely from the biological oxidation of the sludge. At this temperature, a seven day retention period will destroy most pathogens.

thermophilic anaerobic digestion. Anaerobic digestion of sludge over a temperature range of 40°–55°. Not used in the UK.

thermophilic bacteria. Bacteria which are most active in the temperature range 40°–55°C.

thermostatic mixing and diversion valve. A piston-type 3-way valve in the cooling-water circuit of a dual-fuel engine installation which automatically diverts a portion of the flow through coolers if a pre-selected temperature is reached.

thickening. The process by which water is removed from sludge by settlement aided by mechanical stirring or by gas flotation. *See* **consolidation, picket-fence thickener**.

thickening tank. A tank specially designed to thicken sludge by settlement, using a slowly rotating picket-fence thickener the rods of which form void channels through which water is displaced upwards. *See* **consolidation tank**.

thin-layer chromatography. (TLC). Chromatography in which the conventional column is replaced by a thin layer of the solid absorbent spread uniformly on an inert backing such as a glass plate. The sample is applied as a drop near one edge of the plate. That edge is dipped in a suitable solvent which elutes the sample spot upwards. The components move at different rates and are thus separated. The separated spots are located and identified by appropriate tests. *See* **chromatography**.

Thiobacillus thio-oxidans. A sulphur-oxidizing bacterium which, when present in sewers, converts sulphur into sulphuric acid (which in turn attacks concrete) according to the equation:

$$2S + 3O_2 + 2H_2O \xrightarrow[\textit{thio-oxidans}]{\textit{Thiobacillus}} 2H_2SO_4.$$

The bacterium grows best in a strongly acid medium (pH 2.0 — 6.0) and can also oxidize thiosulphate to sulphate, thus:

$$Na_2S_2O_3 + 2O_2 + H_2O \xrightarrow[\textit{thio-oxidans}]{\textit{Thiobacillus}} Na_2SO_4 + H_2SO_4.$$

thixotrophy. A property exhibited by substances including sewage sludge whereby they assume a gel form on standing but liquefy when shaken or stirred.

tidal flap valve. A valve with a hinged disk fitted at the outlet end of a short pipeline discharging to sea which opens when the tide is low and closes by gravity as the tide rises and there is a back-pressure.

tidal waters. Any part of the sea or any part of a river within the ebb and flow of the tide at ordinary spring tides, and not being a harbour.

time of concentration. The longest time taken for the rain falling on a drainage area to travel from the most remote point in a sewerage system to the point under consideration, i.e. a storm overflow or sewage-treatment works. Calculated on the velocity when the sewer is flowing full.

time of entry. The average time taken for rain falling on a drainage area to enter the sewerage system, depending largely on the impermeability of the area and the density of housing.

tipping trough. A simple form of automatic dosing apparatus used in small installations for applying settled sewage to a biological filter. The trough is supported on trunnions and the sewage is discharged into it at one end. When full it overbalances and tips the contents, either directly on to the filter surface or into feed troughs or perforated pipes. A double tipper has two troughs which fill alternately and tip in opposite directions so that the two halves of the filter are dosed in turn.

TNO rotor. *See* **cage rotor**.

top water level. The maximum water level in a sedimentation tank or settlement tank, aeration tank, or a sludge storage tank.

total dissolved solids (TDS). The concentration of dissolved solids in a wastewater or effluent, i.e. the residue after evaporation and drying, expressed in milligrammes per litre of sample.

total head. *See* **head**.

tower filter. *See* **packed tower filter**.

toxicity. A characteristic of a chemical or a mixture of chemicals defining their poisoning effect on an organism. In water all soluble substances are toxic at some concentration, 'toxic substances' usually referring to those showing poisoning effects at relatively low concentrations. 'Acute toxicity' is demonstrated within a short period (hours to days) of exposure; typically associated with the breakdown of tissues/physiological systems, at rates which exceed rates of repair or adaptation. Commonly refers to rapidly lethal effects. 'Chronic toxicity' is of long duration, possibly affecting more than one generation, but the effects are less severe than those observed under conditions of acute poisoning. *See* **toxicity test.**

toxicity test. A controlled test using aquatic organisms (most commonly fish) to determine the harmful effect of a pollutant on aquatic life. *See* **acute toxicity test, chronic toxicity test.**

trace element. A chemical element present in a system, organism, etc., in relatively low concentration.

trade effluent. As defined in the Water Industry Act 1991, Section 141(1); (a) means any liquid, either with or without particles of matter in suspension in the liquid, which is wholly or partly produced in the course of any trade or industry carried on at trade premises; and (b) in relation to any trade premises, means any such liquid which is so produced in the course of any trade or industry carried on at those premises, but does not include domestic sewage.

trade premises. Any premises used or intended to be used for carrying on any trade or industry.

trade waste. *See* **trade effluent.**

travelling-bridge scraper. A type of scraper used in connexion with horizontal-flow tanks, consisting essentially of a power-driven bridge spanning the tank from which is suspended either a vertical or a trailing blade. The bridge traverses the tank on rails, the blade being lowered when sweeping sludge to hoppers or a trough at the inlet end of the tank and raised for the return journey. The bridge is driven by an electric motor and may be rope-hauled, have a rack and pinion drive, or it may be a traction drive on rails. The Mieder scraper, introduced into the UK from Germany about 1932, was the earliest form of travelling-bridge scraper.

travelling distributor. *See* **reciprocating-arm distributor, reciprocating-waterwheel distributor**.

treatability. The relative ease with which the major constituents of an industrial wastewater are assimilated by micro-organisms and broken down in biological treatment processes compared with the constituents of domestic wastewater.

treated sludge. Sludge which has undergone biological, chemical or heat treatment, long-term storage or any other process to reduce significantly its fermentability and the health hazards resulting from its use. (ref. The Sludge (Use in Agriculture) Regulations 1989.)

Trematoda. A class of Platyhelminthes, including flukes. They have organs of attachment consisting of suckers and hooks, and they usually have a complicated life-cycle.

trenching. A method of disposing of liquid sludge on land whereby trenches dug in the soil are partially filled with sludge, the land being ploughed and cultivated after the sludge has dried, thus incorporating it in the soil.

Trent biotic index. *See* **biotic index.**

triangular weir. *See* **V-notch weir.**

triazine. Generic name for group of herbicides, including atrazine, prometryne, propazine, simazine, terbutryne.

Trichoptera. Commonly known as caddis-flies. An order of insects having aquatic larvae some of which characteristically build cases of stone or vegetable matter.

trickling filter. *See* **biological filter**.

trophic level. The position occupied by an organism in the food chain, e.g. green plants occupy the first trophic level, herbivores the second, and carnivores which eat herbivores the third.

trunk sewer. A sewer which receives many tributary branches or discharges from other large sewers and serves a large area.

Tubificidae. A family of aquatic oligochaete worms, common in bottom muds, e.g. *Tubifex*.

tubular biological filter. *See* **rolling tube apparatus**.

tubular pressure filter. A sludge-dewatering system in which dewatering occurs in a series of filter tubes by the formation of a layer of cake on the inner surface of the porous tubes as filtrate is expelled under pressure. The cake is discharged at intervals from the flexible filter tubes by a roller assembly.

Turbellaria. Planarians, or free-living flatworms belonging to the phylum Platyhelminthes. Common in fresh waters but may also be found in sea water.

turbidity. Interference with the passage of light rays through a liquid, caused by the presence of fine suspended matter.

turbulent flow. Flow which varies rapidly in magnitude and direction, being the opposite to streamline flow. Also termed 'eddy flow' or 'sinuous flow'.

turbulent velocity. *See* **critical velocity**.

two-stage alternating filtration. See **alternating double filtration**.

two-stage filtration with effluent recirculation. *See* **recirculation**.

two-stage filtration. A modification of conventional biological filtration in which two filters operate in series.

two-stage sedimentation. The division of primary sedimentation into two stages using two sets of tanks. The bulk of the heavier sludge settles in the first-stage tanks and is removed at more frequent intervals than the smaller amount of watery sludge settling in the second-stage tanks.

two-storey tank. A tank with one or two upper compartments which act as continuous-flow sedimentation tanks. Communicating with these is a lower compartment which receives sludge settling in the upper compartments for storage and to enable it to undergo anaerobic digestion. *See* **Imhoff tank**.

U

Ulothrix. A filamentous green alga, common in fresh waters and on the surface of biological filters.

ultimate oxygen demand (UOD). The calculated amount of oxygen required to oxidize the organic carbon content of discharges to carbon dioxide and the organic and ammoniacal nitrogen to nitrate, expressed in milligrammes per litre.

ultra-filtration. The use of membranes which are more 'open' than those used in reverse osmosis for the further treatment of biologically-treated sewage, but which are fine enough to retain colloids and some large organic molecules.

ultrasonic level detector. The ultrasonic energy emitted from a combined transmitter/receiver installed above the liquid is reflected back from the surface. The time elapsed between transmission and reception of the signal is proportional to the distance travelled, and hence the depth of the liquid can be derived.

ultrasonic sensor and generator. The generator is a device for producing sound energy at frequencies above the upper limits of audibility. The sensor is a specialized microphone sensitive to ultrasonic energy, converting it into electrical impulses which can be detected and amplified by a suitable electronic receiver and subsequently fed to a loudspeaker, meter, or recorder. An underwater sensor is known as a hydrophone. The various forms of combined generator and sensor can be adapted to determine sludge density within pipes, movements of mudbanks and fish shoals (sonar), and individual fish may be tracked by detecting pulses from a 'tag' located in (or on) the fish, using a hydrophone. The tags can be built to emit only on demand (transponder), or continuously at a steady repetition frequency. Other parameters may be measured by varying the pulse rate or the carrier frequency.

ultra-violet lamp. A lamp which emits radiations of wavelength less than 390 nanometres. Used in covered sump wells for controlling odour and on microstrainers for preventing the formation of a biological film, preferably at a temperature not exceeding 21°C.

umbilical sytem. A system of applying sludge to agricultural land by feeding it from a storage tank to a mobile distributor via a hose pulled out from a reel.

underdrain. A line or lines of pipes, sometimes porous, with open joints laid under an area of land used for treating sewage or under a sludge-drying bed or sand filter for collecting the effluent. With a biological filter, special drainage tiles are used for the same purpose.

uniform flow. Flow in which the velocity is the same in both magnitude and direction from point to point along the conduit.

uniformly-mixed system. *See* **complete-mixing system**.

unloading. *See* **sloughing**.

Unox process. A proprietary activated-sludge process, developed in the USA, in which a surface aerator is used for oxygenating the mixed liquor in an oxygen-enriched atmosphere within a series of at least three enclosed tanks in which sewage and recycled sludge enter the first tank and mixed liquor flows from the outlet tank to settlement tanks.

upper explosive limit. *See* **explosive limits**.

upward-flow anaerobic sludge-blanket reactor (UASB). A type of anaerobic contact reactor in which the methane-forming bacteria are present in the form of 'granules' instead of a dispersed mass of organisms.

upward-flow clarifier. A bed of pea gravel supported in a perforated tray or on wedge wire and installed at the outlet end of a secondary settlement tank, the top of the gravel being at least 150 mm below the water surface; the clarifier may be installed in a separate tank. Effluent flows upward through the clarifier and deposited solids are removed by backwashing at regular intervals. A clarifier in which pea gravel is used is also called a 'pebble-bed clarifer' or a

'Banks clarifier' after D.H. Banks, who installed the first at Battle, Sussex, about 1964.

upward-flow sand filter. A sand filter, first used about 1967, for removing suspended solids from a biologically-treated sewage, the liquid being pumped upward through sand and gravel the grading of which becomes finer from bottom to top so that it meets the coarser medium first. There may be a metal retaining grid a little below the surface of the sand to prevent expansion of the bed during filtration. The filter is cleaned by using an air scour and washing in the direction of flow with effluent. The 'Immedium' filter is a type of upward-flow sand filter.

ureas. Generic name for group of herbicides, including chlorotoluron, diuron, isoproturon, linuron.

V

vacuum and pressure relief assembly. An assembly fitted near the inlet end of a pipe conveying gas from a primary digestion tank and containing two valves, one which opens if the pressure of the gas under the cover falls below a specified value, and another which opens if the pressure exceeds a specified value, admitting air or venting gas to maintain the pressure between the specified limits. The assembly may be connected electrically to a panel with warning liqhts and a klaxon, operated by the valves.

vacuum filter. A machine for dewatering sludge. There are various types, e.g. drum, string discharge, belt, coil, or disk. The drum type consists essentially of a cylindrical drum mounted on and revolving about a horizontal axis. The drum is covered with a special cloth and is partially submerged in the sludge to be filtered. A vacuum is maintained under the cloth for the larger part of a revolution to extract moisture.

vacuum filter yield. The rate at which sludge is dewatered on a vacuum filter, expressed in terms of kilogrammes of dry solids per square metre per hour, or in kilogrammes of dry solids per day.

vacuum relief valve. A safety valve that permits air to enter to counteract a vacuum.

vacuum sewerage system. A system developed in Sweden and used since 1959, based on two main principles: (a) the use of air instead of water for transporting the discharge from water closets, using a minimum amount of water, and (b) the separation of 'black' water (excreta and urine) from 'grey' water (all other household liquid wastes). The two liquors are treated separately, the concentrated 'black' water chemically and the 'grey' water biologically. The system relies on the use of vacuum to transport sewage operating at 0.5 bar negative pressure. Sewage flows to a sump and at a predetermined level an interface vacuum valve opens to admit the sewage to the vacuum sewer. The sewage is drawn along the sewer to a reception sump from where it may be pumped into a conventional system. Several systems have been installed in the

UK since 1968, and the main advantages are the shallow depth, small diameter pipes and the elimination of infiltration. They have been installed for small estates, and hospitals and are the preferred system for ships.

valve. A device used for controlling the flow of a liquid by means of an aperture the size of which can be varied by movement of a plate or disc, a gate, a piston, a plug or a ball. *See* **air release valve, check valve, decanting valve, delivery valve, float-operated regulating valve, foot valve, gate valve, plug valve, pressure relief valve, pressure reducing valve, suction valve, tidal flap valve, vacuum relief valve**.

valve actuator. A hydraulic, pneumatic or electric powered unit used for operating a valve by remote control or automatically, sometimes fitted with signal feedback and interlock arrangements and a fail-safe device.

van Kleeck's formula. A formula proposed by van Kleeck of the USA in 1945 for calculating the proportion of the organic matter in sludge which has been decomposed by anaerobic digestion, thus:

$$\text{Reduction (per cent)} = (1 - \frac{M_r \times O_d}{O_r \times M_d}) \times 100,$$

where M_r is the percentage of mineral matter in the raw sludge, O_r the percentage of organic matter in the raw sludge, and M_d the percentage of mineral matter and O_d the percentage of organic matter in the digested sludge.

Vaucheria. A filamentous green algae, common in streams.

V-blade scraper with multiple draw-offs. A type of scraper in radial-flow tanks with flat floors used for separating activated sludge. Each of a series of V-shaped blades extending from the centre to the periphery of the tank has a vertical draw-off pipe with a horizontal extension discharging into a sight box or central outlet so that sludge deposited near the periphery of the tank is evacuated as quickly as sludge deposited near the centre. Sludge is withdrawn by hydrostatic pressure and that due to movement of the scraper or, in large tanks, with the aid of an air-lift pump.

vegetable tanning. Tanning in which vegetable extracts are used, involving immersion of the skins in a tanning liquor containing extracts made from oak bark, chestnut wood, quebracho, sumach or a synthetic material. Wastewaters include spent liquors and washwaters.

velocity coefficient. *See* **coefficient of velocity**.

velocity head. The vertical distance through which a fluid must fall freely under gravity to reach the velocity that it possesses. Equal to the square of the velocity divided by twice the acceleration due to gravity.

velocity of approach. With a rectangular weir or V-notch, the velocity of the liquid at the point where the upstream head is measured.

velocity rod. A rod weighted at the bottom so that it floats in a vertical position. *See* **surface float, sub-surface float**.

vena contracta. The cross-sectional area of a nappe or jet issuing through or over an orifice or weir at the point downstream of the plane of the orifice or weir where the cross-sectional area is at its smallest. The nappe or jet converges to this point and when flowing away, diverges from it.

Venturator. A trade name for a particular venturi-aeration device.

Venturi flume. A flume, introduced by Prof. A.H. Jameson in 1925, used for measuring the flow in an open channel. It consists essentially of a contracting length, a throat, and an expanding length, sometimes combined with a hump on the throat of the flume. The upper and lower heads are each measured at a definite distance from the throat. *See* **standing-wave flume**.

Venturi meter. A device introduced by George Kent Ltd in 1894, used for measuring the flow of liquid in a pipeline, in which there is a gradual contraction to a throat followed by an expansion to normal diameter. The pressure is measured at the throat where the pressure is reduced and upstream where the diameter is normal, small pipes leading to gauges at these points. The velocity and therefore the rate of flow is related to the pressure difference between these points.

vernal slough. *See* **sloughing**.

vertical retort. A retort used in the production of coal gas in which coal enters at the top and coke is withdrawn, sometimes continuously, from the bottom.

viable bacteria. Bacteria which are capable of multiplying.

viruses. Small infectious particles of biological origin. They have a unique structure and method of reproduction. In their simplest form they consist solely of a nucleic acid core surrounded by a protein coat. They are obligate intracellular parasites i.e. they can only multiply inside a living cell of a suitable host. Viruses are classified according to their host, size, antigenic properties and the composition of their nucleic acids.

viscose process. Process used for manufacturing artificial silk from wood pulp, involving the following processes: (a) pulp steeped in solution of caustic soda; (b) pressed to remove alkaline liquor; (c) shredded, mixed with carbon disulphide and dissolved in a solution of caustic soda; (d) solution filtered and de-aerated; (e) solution forced through very fine jets into bath of dilute sulphuric acid containing sodium sulphate, zinc sulphate and certain other materials to assist spinning; (f) filament leaving spinning bath washed with water to remove excess acidic liquor; (g) filament treated with sodium sulphide to remove sulphur; (h) washed with water and, in some cases, bleached. Wastewaters include alkaline pulp liquor, acidic liquors from spinning and washing, alkaline liquor from finishing processes, and wash-waters.

viscosity. The cohesive force existing between particles of a fluid which causes the fluid to offer resistance to a relative sliding motion between particles.

Vitox aerator. A trade name for a proprietary device for dissolving pure oxygen in river water, wastewater or mixed liquor in the aeration tank of an activated-sludge plant.

V-notch weir. A measuring weir of V-shape with the angle at the apex usually 90°, used for measuring small discharges.

void ratio. The ratio of the volume of the voids in the medium of a biological filter to the bulk volume of the medium, expressed as a percentage.

volatile acids. Acids, mainly acetic, propionic and butyric, produced as a result of the liquefaction and hydrolysis of sludge, as during anaerobic digestion. Also described as volatile fatty acids (VFA), especially in monitoring the performance of sludge digesters.

volatile matter. The ratio of the weight of dry matter lost after heating to 600°C to the initial weight, expressed as a percentage. The volatile content of sludge is assumed to indicate its approximate organic content.

vortex grit separator. A grit separating tank with a cylindrical top portion and a conical bottom. The sewage enters tangentially and separation of grit is assisted by an electrically-driven rotating paddle at the base of the cylindrical portion and compressed air issuing from a diffuser ring in the hopper. Grit settling in the hopper is transferred by an air-lift pump to a vortex washer whilst the sewage containing the organic matter overflows a peripheral weir. *See* **vortex grit washer**.

vortex grit washer. A grit washer consisting of a chamber at the centre of which is a cylindrical vortex chamber with an open-ended conical bottom. Water-borne grit from the vortex separator enters the vortex chamber tangentially and is separated from organic matter by centrifugal force, the washed grit falling from the vortex chamber to the floor of the main chamber from whence it is removed by a bucket elevator. The carrier water with the organic matter is withdrawn through a central siphon for return to the sewage flow.

Vorticella. A genus of peritrichous ciliate, common in activated sludge.

W

wash-back. Fermentation vessel used in the manufacture of whisky.

washout. An outlet from a tank or chamber, controlled by a valve which is opened occasionally to release water or sludge.

washwater. Water used for washing the bed of sand in a sand filter or the fabric of a microstrainer.

waste disposal unit. An electrically-operated device fitted to the kitchen sink for disintegrating garbage before it is flushed into the drainage system.

waste-gas burner. A burner, with automatic valve and ignition, used for the disposal of sludge gas in excess of requirements.

waste. (a) any substance which constitutes unwanted material or effluent arising from the application of any process; and (b) any substance or article which requires to be disposed of as being broken, worn out, contaminated, or otherwise spoiled. *See* **sewage, trade effluent**.

water authority. One of ten authorities established under the Water Act 1973 to assume responsibility for water services in England and Wales on 1 April 1974. The functions of the authority included: (a) those formerly exercisable by the river authorities in respect of river pollution, fisheries and land drainage; (b) water conservation and the supply of water within the authority's area (except in an area served by a statutory water authority); (c) sewerage and sewage disposal; (d) duties with regard to recreation, and nature conservation and amenity. Superseded by the NRA and water companies in 1989.

water-borne disease. A disease caused by organisms carried by water. The most common water-borne diseases are typhoid fever, Asiatic cholera, dysentery, and other intestinal disturbances.

water-carriage system. The system of conveying wastewater from buildings by the use of water.

water conservation. The preservation, control and development of water resources (both surface and ground) whether by storage, including natural ground storage, prevention of pollution, or other means, so as to ensure that adequate and reliable supplies of water are made available for all purposes in the most suitable and economical way whilst safeguarding legitimate interests.

water content. The weight of water in sludge per unit weight of sludge, expressed as a percentage.

water hammer. A hammering sound in a pipeline caused by a violent surge of pressure due to a sudden interruption in the flow, e.g. a valve being closed too rapidly.

water hog (log) louse. *Asellus aquaticus*, a crustacean found in fresh water and a useful indicator of organic enrichment.

water pollution control works. *See* **sewage-treatment works**.

Water Pollution Research Laboratory. A laboratory set up by the Water Pollution Research Board, which was formed in 1927, to investigate the treatment and disposal of domestic and industrial wastewaters, and the effects and prevention of pollution of surface waters and underground water. The Laboratory maintained a library containing literature on water pollution control and prepared abstracts of current literature. Under the major reorganization of the water industry the Laboratory became part of the Water Research Centre in 1974. *See* **Water Research Association, Water Research Centre**.

water-quality monitoring. The use of monitors housed at the side of the stream or river and measuring against a standard such quality parameters as dissolved oxygen, ammonia, suspended solids, and organic carbon. The monitoring may be automatic or continuous, or both. *See* **water-quality surveillance**.

water-quality standards. Standards applicable to a surface water receiving domestic and industrial effluents.

water quality states. An ordered set of 'significant ranges' of concentration of constituents describing the quality of a water resource with which a particular benefit or cost function is associated; over which the function is sensibly constant and is different from any other set of ranges. A significant range is determined by (a) the effect on the use of the river water of the concentration of the constituents, and (b) the cost of treating that particular range of concentration when water is abstracted from the river. A concept suggested by D.H. Newsome for use in the Trent Economic Model.

water-quality surveillance. The measurement of quality parameters such as dissolved oxygen, ammonia, suspended solids, and organic carbon. Measurement may be automatic or continuous, or both. *See* **water-quality monitoring**.

Water Research Association. A central research organization set up by the water industry in 1953 to conduct research into water resources, treatment and distribution, and to provide information and technical liaison services for member organizations. Under the 1974 reorganization of the water industry the Association's laboratory became part of the Water Research Centre. *See* **Water Pollution Research Laboratory**, **Water Research Centre**.

Water Research Centre. An organization set up following the Water Act 1973 to be responsible for research and development in the reorganized water industry, consisting of the Water Pollution Research Laboratory, Water Research Association, and part of the technology division of the Water Resources Board. The organization was turned into a limited company when the water industry in England and Wales was privatized in 1989. *See* **Water Pollution Research Laboratory**, **Water Research Association**.

waterwheel-driven distributor. *See* **reciprocating-arm ditributor**.

wedge wire panels. A trade name for panels fabricated from aluminium or stainless steel wedge wire, or wire of wedge cross-section with the upstream end wider than the downstream end to prevent blockage, the spaces being from 0.5 mm to 1.25 mm wide. First used experimentally about 1961 instead of media for sludge-drying beds, and later in upward-flow clarifiers.

Weil's disease. Leptospiral jaundice, caused by a spirochaete and transmitted to human beings by sewer rats and their urine. *See* ***Leptospira icterohaemor-rhagiae***.

weir. A structure over which water flows, the downstream level of the water usually being lower than the sill of the weir. When used for measuring flows the weir may be rectangular, notched or trapezoidal and the rate of flow will be related to the upstream height of the water above the sill and to the geometry of the weir opening. *See* **overflow weir**, **peripheral weir**, **rectangular weir**, **scum weir**, **storm-sewage diversion weir**, **submerged weir**, **V-notch weir**.

weir overflow rate. The volume of liquid passing over the outlet weir of a tank per unit length of weir at maximum flow, calculated as follows:

$$\text{Weir overflow rate (m}^3/\text{m d)} = \frac{\text{maximum rate of flow (m}^3/\text{d)}}{\text{total length of outlet weirs (m)}}$$

weir penstock. A device incorporating a vertically sliding gate so designed that liquid flows over the top.

wet-air oxidation. A process introduced by F.J. Zimmermann of the USA in 1954 for conditioning sludge prior to dewatering in which the sludge is pressurized, air is introduced and the sludge/air mixture passes through heat exchangers in which its temperature is raised to 125°-140°C. Steam is now injected to raise its temperature to 160°–200°C. The mixture then passes through a reactor which provides a sufficient period of retention to accomplish the desired oxidation and heat treatment. Gas and steam are separated from the sludge before it passes to a storage tank. Also known as the 'Zimpro process' and 'conditioning with air'.

wet pressure loss. The wet pressure loss during passage of air through a porous diffuser is defined as the resistance of the wet saturated diffuser when passing a definite volume of air per unit of time. It is measured by subtracting the depth of water column over the diffuser, in millimetres, from the pressure, in millimetres of water, required to force the definite volume of air through the diffuser in the unit of time.

wet scrubbing. The wetting of finely-divided solids carried in suspension in exhaust gases with sprays of water so that they can be removed in a cyclone.

wet well. The compartment or sump in a pumping station which receives the sewage or sludge to be pumped and to which the suction pipes of the pumps are connected.

wetted perimeter. The length of the wetted boundary of a pipe, sewer or channel at a cross section, measured at right angles to the flow.

white liquor. When pulp is being manufactured from wood, the liquor containing the ash of the spent lye after being causticized with lime.

white sour. Final treatment of cotton goods with weak acid prior to bleaching.

white water. Wastewater from a paper machine, containing fibre and probably clay, dye and pigment. It is extremely turbid water — white in appearance due to reflection by entrained air and the presence of fibre, clay, etc. Also termed 'backwater'.

Willett pump. A proprietary make of reciprocating pump used for forcing sludge into a pressure filter, the pressure building up as pressing proceeds.

windrowing. A method of composting sewage sludge by stacking sludge cake, with or without a bulking agent, into a long, low ridge which is not artificially aerated but which is normally turned mechanically at intervals.

wire-rope screen. *See* **rope-band screen**.

wool scouring. Washing of raw wool to remove impurities by moving it through a series of tanks, or 'bowls', in counterflow to a stream of water. Detergents, or soap and soda ash, added to first bowl or sometimes to more than one bowl. Wastewater, called 'wool-scouring liquor', is a hot, alkaline, brown, turbid, greasy and highly putrescible liquor.

wool suds. A term sometimes used for wool-scouring liquor.

works liquors. Liquors produced on a sewage-treatment works. Such liquors include the contents of storm and other tanks when they are emptied, liquor separated from digested sludge in secondary digestion tanks, storage tanks or lagoons, and liquor separated from sludge during conditioning or dewatering.

wort. Liquor produced as a result of steeping malt in water to convert starch to sugar by enzymic action.

Y

yarn, piece and blanket scouring. Removal of natural or added oils by scouring, usually with a solution containing detergent, or soap and soda ash, and washing with water. Ammonia and fuller's earth may also be used. Wastewaters include scouring liquor and washwaters.

yeast manufacture. Yeast is made by fermenting molasses after inoculation with 'wort' grown previously under carefully controlled conditions. It is used in brewing and bread making. Wastewaters include spent wort and washwaters.

yolk. Animal secretions in raw wool of sheep and lambs. Also termed 'suint'.

Z

Zimmermann process. *See* **wet-air oxidation**.

Zimpro process. *See* **wet-air oxidation**.

zinc equivalent. The sum of the copper, zinc and nickel contents of a sludge in milligrammes per kilogramme, after multiplying the copper content by 2 and the nickel content by 8. Used to indicate the rate of addition of metals and the cumulative concentration in the soil with reference to the effect on the growth of crops. A maximum safe limit of 250 mg/kg zinc equivalent in dry top soil has been suggested.

Zoogloea ramigera. A bacterium which grows embedded in a common gelatinous matrix, forming a bacterial slime. A member of the family Pseudomonadaceae. Common as a slime in biological filters and in flocs of activated sludge.

zoogloeal film. A mass of bacteria embedded in a mucilaginous matrix which covers the wetted surfaces of the medium in a mature biological filter.

zooplankton. Animal plankton, e.g. *Daphnia* (water fleas).

zootoxic. A substance which is toxic to animals.

zwitterion. An ion that carries charges of opposite sign so that it is effectively neutral.

Printed by The Lavenham Press Ltd, Lavenham, Suffolk, England.